MW00612830

MENTAL ILLNESS

A SUPPORT GUIDE

FOR FAMILIES AND FRIENDS

STEPHEN JACOBS

Copyright © 2014 Stephen Jacobs

All rights reserved. This book may not be reproduced, transmitted, or distributed in any form, in whole or in part, without the express written permission of the author.

Stephen Jacobs
SupportandHeal.com

ISBN: 978-0-9915045-1-0

ISBN: 978-0-9915045-0-3 (Kindle)
ISBN: 978-0-9915045-4-1 (ePub)

This book is dedicated to those who suffer from mental illness, and to their families, friends and caregivers who suffer with them.

Table of Contents

Foreword 7

Acknowledgements 9

Part I: Hanging On to Yourself in the Midst of Tragedy 11

1. The Nightmare Begins 13

2. Living in No Man's Land 23

3. Guilt and Blame: The Silent Assasins 37

4. The Five Stages of Grief 55

Part II: Discovering the Strength Within to Survive, Heal and Transcend 59

5. Cutting Away the Stigma of Mental Illness 61

6. Challenging the Interpretation of the Illness 71

7. Discovering the Wisdom Within 83

8. Creating Your Personal Safety Zone 91

9. Negotiating the Legal Quagmire 97

10: Making Difficult Decisions from Within 105

11. Finding Calm in the Eye of the Storm 115

**Part III: Setting the Stage for the Rest of
Your Life** 125

12. Living from Your Center 127

13. Embracing Forgiveness: A New Perspective 133

14. Counting the Blessings in this Disaster 141

15. Drawing on the Power of Gratitude 147

16. Rewriting Our Story 151

17. Creating Your New Life 157

Epilogue 161

Foreword

The current climate of increasing awareness of the needs of the mentally ill has been helpful but still woefully inadequate in treating and caring for those afflicted with these debilitating conditions. As slow progress is being made in this arena, the toll of psychiatric debilitation on those that care for and are invested in the person afflicted is slowly coming to light. Throughout my career it has been painful for me to observe the turmoil and helplessness of these caregivers as they witness the mental decline of someone they love and the impact it has had on their lives.

This is a book about the stress of the families and caregivers of the mentally ill, and represents a fresh and genuinely useful approach to repositioning this tragic event within a families' understanding. The good news is that not only does it document the trials of the caregivers and families, but offers tools to help reduce the stress and increase the ability of the caregiver or family member to survive, and in some odd way even thrive in the process.

Stephen Jacobs is in a unique position to help others as they go through the trials of losing the one they love to the ravages of mental illness. He watched his wife of ten years transform from a healthy functioning partner, to a person who became increasingly unpredictable and unreachable as the illness progressed.

His many years of self-improvement work—before his wife exhibited signs of erratic behavior—helped him to process his emotions and to renegotiate life as his world changed. By using the strategies he imparts in this book, not only did he weather this trauma, but in the process gained an internal sense of balance and resilience.

This book offers a powerful way of diminishing the psychological and physical toll that caring for a loved one with mental illness can create. The retelling of his personal experience, along with the strategies he used to recover himself, are a potent combination that can help others. These deceptively simple exercises offer a step-by-step guide that can help caregivers grow and eventually thrive through the experience. The insights in this book may help decrease the collateral damage to the care-giving family and friends. It provides not only a way to survive, but to regain health, and perhaps become a stronger more integrated person in the process.

Charles S. Price, M.D.
Clinical Professor of Psychiatry
University of Nevada, Reno
September 2014

Acknowledgements

I wish to thank all those who have assisted me with this project: Jennifer Field for the initial insight that I possessed something which could alleviate suffering, and it needed to be shared; fellow author, Betty Edwards, who helped with the organization and general structure of the material; editors Bob LeGoy and John Michals; self-publication assistance, Pat Barnes; and most importantly my partner, Rosie Bedell, who offered encouragement and support at every stage.

Part I

Hanging On to Yourself in the Midst of Tragedy

1

The Nightmare Begins

"There is a woman in our yard who has come to kill me."

With these words, my wife of 10 years announced her mental illness. Her eerie intonation made me shiver. Despite the dim light I could see the panic on her face.

I had fallen asleep with my arms wrapped around Julie, my wife. Three hours later I was awakened by a frightening stranger.

"What?" I said, half asleep. "What woman? What are you talking about?" My hands began to perspire and my heart was pounding. "Julie, what's going on? Were you having a nightmare?"

She rolled out of bed onto the floor and began crawling on her belly toward the bathroom. I slipped out of the other side of the bed and rushed after her.

"Get down!" she screeched in a voice I had never heard before. "She'll see you!" A few moments later we were both sitting on the cold bathroom floor. "Julie, who will see me?"

"Your lover, Anna, you coward! You think I don't know what you two have been planning?"

It took all of my strength to try to appear calm. My mind was racing out of control as I said slowly and softly: "Julie, there is no one in our yard. I don't have another lover. I love you. You are my only lover."

"Don't lie to me" she said, her face flushed, stern and unloving. "I know what you are planning and you won't get away with it."

I told her again that there was no one in our yard, that I had no other lover, that we were safe. I told her I would never do anything to hurt her. I asked her to remember our life together and all that we had shared.

"Julie, has there ever been a single moment when I behaved like you are describing? You must have had a nightmare. There is no one in our yard. No one has come to kill you."

My logical response made her more agitated and angry.

"Stop lying" she hissed, trying to keep her voice subdued, but unable to hide her rage and disgust.

I looked at Merlin, our little Jack Russell Terrier, who had joined us. He seemed as confused as I was. Why we were out of bed in the middle of the night, sitting on the cold floor without our clothes? Why were we using only the night light instead of turning on the bathroom lights as we typically did? Why were we crawling on our hands and knees rather than standing up and walking erect? Why were we whispering rather than speaking in our normal voices?

Two hours later Julie called the police. My desperate attempts to bring her back to reality had failed. I decided to walk around the house with a flashlight, thinking it might reassure her. Instead she imagined I was signaling my lover with the light. "The police are on their way and you are going to jail" she declared.

I gave up. Everything I said or did was only making the situation worse. I was completely unable to reason with the person whom I knew best. I felt totally alone in a relationship which had always comforted me. For the first time in our relationship, I felt genuine fear in her presence.

As I sat at our dining room table, waiting for the police to arrive, I felt sick and could not think clearly. I was in serious mental and emotional overload. I was confused, anxious and uncertain what I should do. In a way, I was glad that Julie had called the police. The situation was beyond my ability to resolve. Professional help was on the way.

From Julie's perspective, she had narrowly escaped being murdered. Her unfaithful husband had been caught in the act and would soon be punished.

Though for different reasons, we each were relieved when a policeman rang our doorbell at 4 a.m. Julie met him at the door. He looked inside and saw me sitting at the table. "Mr. Jacobs, please remain inside your house while I visit with your wife."

I was left to try to find some insight that might explain Julie's meltdown. I felt like I was spinning; I was nauseous. I couldn't comprehend what was happening. It seemed like a dream, a story someone else had made up. Yet somehow I was now in it, acting it out.

After speaking with Julie for a few minutes, the patrolman placed her into his patrol car. Then he came into the house for my version of the story. After a brief conversation he called for paramedics. When they arrived they did a short evaluation, ordered an ambulance and transported Julie to the hospital.

Thus began a cold, confusing chapter in my life. It was April 26, 2005, a morning I would never forget.

How This Book Came To Be

At the time of Julie's crisis, I had been a meditation instructor for almost 25 years. As a consequence, I had developed many skills for coping with stress. Yet my background seemed to be of only modest value; I felt completely overwhelmed.

Over time, to counteract my feeling of disconnectedness, I began to make conscious use of the skills, techniques and strategies I had learned in numerous seminars and workshops over this 25 year period. When I approached my problem this way, my stress level began to decrease. It was not easy and it did not happen overnight, but by utilizing my own background, I moved through this desperate event in a way which systematically returned me to wholeness.

I never expected to write a book about my experience; I never thought of myself as an author. But one day I realized that the strategies I had used to help myself could be structured in a way that would assist others with similar problems. As I looked back on my personal restoration, I realized I had transitioned from hopeless and despondent to alive and optimistic. I had not only survived, but healed. I felt peaceful, contented and happy. This insight was the beginning of this book.

This Guidebook is a consequence of my own healing experience, combined with more than five years of research. But I did not do the research from the perspective of a university professor academically studying symptoms. I did it from the mindset of someone who survived, healed, and transcended a specific situation. I have taken this journey back to wholeness. For this reason I know that you can take it too.

I gave a rough draft of the book to a psychiatrist friend. I wanted professional feedback. After reviewing the document he said: "Many of these techniques are what we would utilize in private therapy with a family member who has a mental illness in their family." But often, he said, professionals are unable to treat a patients' family as a unit, because medical insurance will not cover the visits. Thus the family is left to do the best they can on their own. "This situation is far from ideal," he said, "so this Guidebook would be a valuable resource for anyone who is currently dealing with mental illness in their family."

Given this encouragement, I interviewed additional psychiatrists, psychologists, and therapists. I also spoke with many people who either have or had mental illness, and with their families and friends. This book is the result of my research.

But this book is it not about how a mentally ill person might be helped back to stability and balance. I leave that to health care professionals. Rather this book is intended to support those who are living with someone with a mental illness (regardless of whether they are physically under the same roof). If you are dealing with someone who has a mental illness, then this Guidebook is for you.

Why This Guidebook Will Work

There is an old riddle: "You can't get there from here. Where are you?"

Answer: "You are lost!"

If you have a loved one with a mental illness, this probably describes how you feel—lost. This was how I felt, like a ship without an anchor, being blown in the direction of the prevailing wind, subject to change at any moment.

But today I am happy, feel empowered, and enjoy my life again. This book describes how I recovered and regained my sense of self. It is designed to take you, step by step, back to your sense of power and contentment.

Here is why it will work for you:

Almost everyone can learn to drive a car, ride a bicycle, or read a book. But there are techniques to each of these skills. Once we have such skills, however, accomplishment of the goal is automatic. A first grade teacher, for instance, can confidently tell new students that if they pay attention to the instructions and do the required homework, they will soon be able to read. It is not guesswork. It is not luck. It does not apply to some but not to others. Almost everyone can learn to read.

Even if the specifics of mental illness within your family, business setting, or social setting do not change or improve, this book will provide you with a toolset which can be used to help regain your stability.

To be an effective caregiver (or just a caring friend), it is necessary that we retain control of *our lives*. This can be an enormous challenge when someone we love becomes ill. This Guidebook rests on the premise that nothing on the outside needs to change in order to regain our sense of power, balance and enthusiasm. The change this book will facilitate is on the *inside*; therefore it depends only upon our willingness.

In a way, it's like flying on a commercial airliner. To paraphrase one of the safety instructions: If an oxygen mask drops from the overhead compartment above your seat, put your mask on first—then assist others. The reasoning is clear: If you don't save yourself, you won't be able to help others.

The goal of this book is to provide you—as a caregiver—with mental, emotional and psychological support. Not only will your personal stress be lessened, but you also will become more capable of assisting others.

Get the Most from This Guidebook

This Guidebook is based upon what happened to me. The real value, however, will be to understand the concepts presented—then apply them to your situation. For this reason, each chapter will deal with a particular topic, followed by an Exercise. Each Exercise is designed to help you anchor the information. It is not enough to understand the ideas that are presented; they need to be "activated" by bringing them into your own unique circumstance. I therefore encourage you to be diligent about completing each Exercise as you come to it.

Use a large Notebook to record all of your answers, plus any additional notes and ideas that occur to you as you work through this material. Your Notebook will become a personal journal, a place where you can be completely honest with yourself. (For this reason you may want to keep it where only you will have access to it.)

Many people go through this Guidebook—or certain parts of it—multiple times. If you do so you may respond differently to some questions at a later time. This progress is always fascinating and can provide its own motivation to continue working with the concepts you will be learning.

Many of the ideas and Exercises can be a resource for you even beyond the situation of mental illness in your family. Happiness, contentment, and feelings of love and connectedness have no limit. They are in infinite supply and they can grow and expand over a lifetime. Regardless of how you might feel as you read this Guide, and how far away happiness may appear, there are steps you can take that will point you back home.

Sometimes a plant just needs a bit of fertilizer and water to grow more healthy, more productive, and more beautiful. The plant has an innate ability to do this; it just needs the proper conditions to support its growth. This Guidebook will help you to create an environment conducive to your own balance and health.

Information in some chapters may seem redundant; this is by design. Repeating information (in a different way) creates new mental connections. Some of these concepts, when applied and integrated, will help to restructure the neural pathways in your brain, and consequently create a new understanding of a life event.

You should begin to feel better after the first few Exercises. But the overall process takes time, so be patient with yourself. This feeling will amplify as you progress through the material.

You may be reading this book soon after a mental illness occurred in your family, or it may be years later. The information is timeless. Many readers, who grew up in a home environment where a parent or sibling was mentally ill, have found great relief, and a sense of completion, after taking this healing journey—even decades later. We carry all of the hurt, misunderstanding, anger and guilt with us until we are able to release it. The fact this book is in your hands indicates you are ready for the journey. If you move through this book with an openness to new ideas, new ways of interpreting, and new ways of understanding, I am certain that you will begin to recover your sense of peace and balance.

If you're ready, let's get started.

_____

Exercise 1: How Did Reading Chapter 1 Affect You?

When you read about my "nightmare experience" earlier in this chapter, how did it make you feel?

Did it create any feelings of anxiety or depression because it reminded you of your own situation? Did it create a feeling of hopefulness and relief to know that someone who has mental illness in their family wrote a book to help others in a similar situation?

Did you not feel anything at all? Is it a bit hard to describe what you felt?

Is it possibly a combination of many different flavors or feelings or emotions?

Please reflect upon this question for a few minutes. Close your eyes and ask yourself the question: "What did I feel?" or "What do I feel?" about the narrative from Chapter 1. There is no correct answer and there is no incorrect answer. Whatever answer comes to you is perfect.

Don't try to censor anything. Whatever you feel is what you feel. I created this Exercise to get you started on the path of noticing how ideas or information make you feel. There is nothing more to it than that.

Please use your Notebook to record any ideas
or insights that you had.

_____

2
Living in No Man's Land

My life was forever changed by my wife's mental illness—in ways that I could never have anticipated. I was 56 years old, yet I knew relatively little about mental illness, much less how to help Julie.

When I looked at my new situation I saw nothing but problems. There was no family support system available to us. We were new to Reno, having moved to Nevada a few months prior to Julie's breakdown. Neither of us had full time work. We had no health insurance. We had no family doctor. I felt like I was stranded in No Man's Land.

The Miriam-Webster dictionary defines No Man's Land as: 1) an area of un-owned, unclaimed, or uninhabited land; 2) an unoccupied area between opposing armies; 3) an area not suitable or used for occupation or habitation. That seemed an apt description: I was living in a desolate, hostile territory filled with unknown dangers.

I had been trained as a chaplain at my church and had been a featured speaker many times on a range of self-help topics. I had made a variety of radio and TV appearances over the years—but none of this helped me. In retrospect, I discovered that I was experienced at supporting other people with their life challenges, but not very skilled at supporting myself. I found myself completely bewildered by my new circumstance.

My career for many years had been as a businessman. While working as a Human Resource Consultant I had studied personal development for decades. I was particularly drawn to ideas concerning the unused potential of the human mind. That was an ironic aspect of my situation that I overlooked initially.

I was also a meditation instructor, and had attended dozens of self-development seminars. I had become expert at remaining calm, balanced and in control. Yet here I was, out of control and unable to effect the changes that I desired. What I most desired was to have my life returned to normal.

After Julie's initial break with reality, she was released from the hospital the same day with a diagnosis of sleep deprivation. I was incredibly relieved to hear that the problem was something manageable and innocuous. The cure seemed obvious. We would watch only sedate TV shows, have an early dinner, read something uplifting or listen to some good music. Julie could have a long hot bath, a cup of hot milk, and all would be perfect again.

Today I smile at my naiveté.

Within two weeks Julie was back in the hospital, this time in Las Vegas. We had planned a car trip to Sedona, Arizona, for her birthday; Las Vegas was a stopover. Wondering whether or not we should even be going, I consulted the doctor that Julie was seeing. He was ambivalent, but I decided a get-a-way might be good for her. She had not really "come back" from her "night on the bathroom floor" incident 11 days earlier, but she was not outwardly delusional either. She just seemed quiet, subdued.

Julie really wanted to go to Sedona, and so did I. I remember thinking to myself, "Maybe if we can get away from our familiar surroundings for a few days we can put all of this behind us."

24

But we didn't get far. A few hours into the journey, her delusions re-started. She thought I was planning to meet up with my lover somewhere along the way. Julie also decided that my lover was involved in a pornography ring, and that consequently I was going to be surprised when we crossed the state border.

"You're going to be arrested," Julie screamed at me. "You don't know what this woman is involved with. The police and the CIA have been following her. You are implicated in all of this because of your involvement with her. You stupid bastard! What were you thinking?"

She talked nonstop for hours, until out of sheer exasperation I finally yelled back: "Shut up, Julie! We'll see what happens when we get to the border. If you are right, then I deserve to go to jail. But if the police are not waiting for me, then you are mistaken. Do you understand?"

I might as well have remained silent. The woman sitting beside me was a complete stranger. I was trying to reason with her, not comprehending that that was impossible. We had always been able to talk easily about everything. Now, in this desperate circumstance, I was not able to get through to her at all.

"You stupid asshole," she shouted at me. "I don't know why I ever married you. I hate you and I hate what you have done. You won't get away with this. You are going to spend the rest of your life in prison for your crimes against humanity."

My heart was torn apart by this deranged outburst from my wife's lips. None of this could come from the person I knew. My mind began to drift as I remembered the early days with Julie. She was always soft spoken, calm, refined, and willing to listen to others. She was beautiful, both physically and as a personality. She had a compassionate nature, and always seemed able to see the highest in others, and in the world as a whole.

As we drove, my mind reviewed what I knew about my now, mentally unbalanced wife. After an early divorce at age 20—and with the responsibility of a young son—she began a career in the telecommunications industry. Initially she worked as a linesman, climbing utility poles. She was one of the first women to have such a position; at that time it was thought of as a man's job. Twenty years later she retired as Director of Marketing with one of the largest telecommunications companies.

This upward trajectory displayed itself in every area of her life. She was one of those rare individuals who seemingly could accomplish anything. She was brilliant, intuitive, likeable, motivated, and she easily ascended to the top of any group.

When I met her in the early 90's, she was working as an energetic healer. Energetic healing is an umbrella term for any therapy that manipulates the energy circuits in our bodies to regain balance and facilitate our body's innate healing mechanisms. (Therapies such as acupuncture and reflexology would be examples.)

She was able to use her understanding of the body, and how energy moves within it, to help people achieve better health. Her healing career blossomed after a nine year old with terminal kidney cancer, whom the doctors could no longer help, recovered after seeing her. Her reputation spread due to the enthusiasm and thankfulness of this young child's mother. When I met Julie she had a prospective-patient waiting list of three months.

She never lost interest in energetic healing, but after taking an adult education art class she began another career as an artist. Although she never studied art formally, her work soon gained acclaim. It was particularly admired by other accomplished artists. One prominent painter—whose art pieces are displayed in galleries all over the world and cost more than $10,000 each—offered to trade any single piece of her art, for any one of Julie's.

My mind slammed back to our current reality when I pulled into a restaurant, about halfway between Reno and Las Vegas. Our ability to communicate had completely dissolved; Julie would not even sit with me at the table. "I don't eat with people who are in a pornography ring, Steve," she told me. "Does it make you feel powerful to involve children and animals in your sick fantasies? You disgust me."

We had planned to spend the night in Las Vegas. By the time we arrived, I was exhausted, but Julie was still going strong. She seemed to have boundless energy. I decided to wait and see how she was doing in the morning, before taking action. My optimism (or denial) suggested she might still be suffering from a lack of sleep. Perhaps the travel had put added strain on her. In retrospect, I was looking for any reason to believe this was not a serious medical condition.

But Julie awoke the next morning even more aggressive, belligerent, and delusional. I left her at the motel on the pretense of going out to refuel the car. I pulled into a vacant parking lot and phoned the Reno Mental Hospital, where she had been admitted twelve days earlier. I couldn't think of anything else to do. Trying to steady my voice, I asked the nurse, "Do you think I should try to drive her back to Reno, or should I try to find some medical assistance here in Las Vegas"?

The nurse was adamant. "Get help where you are. Is she suicidal? Get her to a hospital as quickly as you can. Do not try to return home; she might open the car door and jump out."

Taking the nurse's advice, I drove to the nearest hospital and explained my situation to the nurse on duty. "If I drive up to the emergency entrance," I said, "do you have a couple of big guys that can help me get her checked in? She won't want to be admitted. She thinks I am the crazy one, waiting to run off with an imaginary lover."

The nurse shook her head. "Legally we are not allowed to do that. If your wife is unwilling to be admitted, then you will need to call 911 and have the paramedics come and evaluate her. If they think she needs treatment they will have her brought in."

By the time I returned to the motel, Julie was not in our room, or in the lobby. I found her in the parking lot. She was walking in circles, talking to herself.

I ran up to the clerk at the front desk, cutting ahead of several people waiting in line, and blurted out, "My wife has flipped out and needs to get to the hospital. I need to call 911. Can I use your phone? This is an emergency!"

The clerk reluctantly handed me a cordless phone. I dialed 911, explained my situation to the emergency operator and heard, "Stay with her. Don't lose sight of her. It will take a few minutes for the paramedics to get there." The dispatcher asked for other details such as the name of our motel and what Julie was wearing. "Do you think she might be dangerous?" the dispatcher asked.

As I spoke with the dispatcher, Julie wandered toward some restaurants and shops. I told the woman on the phone: "I'm on a cordless phone, not a cell phone. I don't know when I might lose my connection. If I lose you, I'll continue to follow her. Tell the paramedics to circle around a bit and try to find us."

I explained that I could not get close to Julie because she might run. "She thinks I have the mental problem, and that I want to put her away so I can be with an imaginary lover."

"The paramedics are almost there," the dispatcher told me. "Don't lose her."

Just then a police car came into sight and Julie bolted. The dispatcher passed information to the patrol unit and the officers quickly apprehended her. Paramedics, arriving soon afterward, examined Julie and an ambulance transported her to the hospital.

A part of me felt relieved to know that my wife was safe. Another part of me felt devastated as we began round two—a new hospital in a new city.

This time Julie spent a week in the hospital. I visited her several times each day. She didn't understand what was happening. "Why can't I go home?" she would ask plaintively. "Why am I in this place with all of these strangers? Some of these people have real problems." Then she would become belligerent: "Have you been with your lover? I know that's why you put me here."

Doctors, nurses and social workers bustled in and out of her room during those days. I remember a particular social worker who spent time talking to Julie the first day. Afterward the woman conferred with me in a waiting room.

"Mr. Jacobs, I am going to read some descriptions out of the Diagnostic and Statistical Manual of Mental Disorders. I want you to tell me which of these descriptions most closely resembles your wife's recent behavior."

I cringed as she went down the list; the descriptions were frightening. Two that closely fitted Julie's behavior were bipolar disorder and paranoid schizophrenia.

Back at the motel, I began to research these diseases. The more I learned, the more disheartened I became. I began to envision a bleak future. This was not a pretty diagnosis and it did not have a simple or clear remedy.

When Julie was finally released, and we returned home, she seemed more stable. But she still did not act like her former self. Even under the influence of the medications, she remained convinced that I had a lover.

What I wanted, of course, was not only for Julie's life to return to its previous pattern, but for mine to do the same. Julie was the one with the illness, but my life was also deeply affected.

If I had been asked, I would have said I didn't care if some of Julie's personality traits never returned. I loved her as a person; I accepted her as I found her. I'd settle for our situation to just be livable again.

But that didn't happen. There were additional hospital visits over the next year. Each time she returned home I would be filled with hope that our life might regain its previous balance. I wanted to believe that this time she had turned the corner and would soon recover.

Unfortunately, within a few weeks of every hospital release, my dream of normality would implode. Rather than getting better, Julie was getting worse. Each delusional episode was more forceful than the previous.

As an example, she found some small plastic toys—the type that once came in cereal boxes—in a kitchen cupboard in the house we were renting. "Why are you playing with these evil spirits, Steve?" Julie asked. "Is your lover impressed by this occult worship?"

"Julie," I said, "these are just plastic toys. Probably the last family who lived here had small children. I didn't know they were in the cupboard. Let's just throw them away."

Rather than reassure her, my explanation challenged her distorted reality. "If you would just tell me the truth," she responded, "maybe I could trust you again." Her eyes were angry. She looked for something to throw at me. "Do you think I am stupid? Do you think I don't know what you are doing? Do you think you are fooling anyone with this voodoo you and your lover are playing with?"

It was a cutting pain to ride up and down with Julie's mood swings. I continued to hope that a lost treasure would be returned. But that was increasingly unlikely. I was frustrated by a lack of useful information. Because of the privacy laws governing doctor patient care, I had no access to her psychiatrist. I knew that Julie went to see a doctor, but had no input or feedback regarding her treatment. One day, exasperated, I drove down to the mental hospital, determined to find some answers.

"I don't know if you remember me," I told the receptionist, "but my wife was a resident here about two months ago. She is starting to behave abnormally again." I explained that I wanted to know what might be done *now*, before Julie once again became extremely unbalanced. The receptionist relayed my story to a psychiatric nurse.

As I talked to the nurse, I described the circumstance of Julie going in for treatment, being released, backsliding, and eventually becoming completely erratic. "When that happens, I have to call 911 and have her readmitted," I said.

It appeared ridiculous to me that there should be these weeks of waiting while my wife got worse. The pattern had repeated itself enough I could tell when she was sliding downhill.

Julie would not stay on her meds and would not keep her appointments at the health clinic. She still insisted that I was trying to have her put away so that I could run off with my imaginary lover. Because of her delusions, any suggestion I made was viewed with suspicion.

I remember asking the nurse: "What would you do if you were in my shoes?" "Mr. Jacobs," she responded, "I'm so sorry for your wife and your situation. I know it is difficult to watch someone you love self-destruct prior to getting help. But unless she is willing to receive treatment, the law does not allow for intervention."

The nurse went on to explain that the only exceptions would be if Julie was deemed a danger to herself or to others, or if she was considered unable to care for herself. "Apart from these exceptions, there is really nothing that a family member can do. I am very sorry."

I left the hospital in a state of despair. The most powerful country in the world—the country that put people on the moon in my lifetime—apparently did not have a clue how to deal effectively with mental illness. The professional mandate was to just watch while my beloved regressed—until she became so dysfunctional she would meet the legal criteria for commitment.

Most people take better care of their cars and houseplants!

The interview with the psychiatric nurse was my lowest point. I realized that day no one else would help me. Worse, no one could help Julie. Both of our lives were adrift. The difference was that I knew that my life had gone astray. I wondered if the circumstance of mental illness might somehow be easier on the one with the disease. I felt the weight and impact of it all of the time; she felt it only some of the time—or so I imagined.

But I also realized that the only person who was going to help me was me. It was an irony. I had spent much of my life accumulating and using information to help others. I had a large collection of techniques and understandings I had accumulated over decades. I had taken dozens of workshops, read hundreds of books and even taught courses. Yet now I felt desperate; I had used much of this material to help myself and others at different times in my life, but never with something so extreme and all-encompassing.

I wish I could tell you that within a few days, weeks, or months my life had returned to normal, but that was not the case. Julie has never fully recovered. She currently lives in a professional facility that specializes in care for her particular disorder.

She and I eventually divorced, but we maintain a loving relationship. I speak with her frequently. This particular life chapter created a sadness which can still bring tears to my eyes. But my journey back to wholeness began right there—right in the midst of this disastrous train wreck!

Exercise 2: The First Rays of Sunlight

Here is a simple-yet-potent Exercise —one that you can use right away. It only takes a few seconds and you might feel positive results immediately:

Whenever you feel upset about anything—anything at all—feel it fully. Take several deep breaths and sink deeply into your emotion—whether it is anger, confusion, frustration, disappointment or sadness.

Close your eyes—at least initially until you have some experience with this process. Closing your eyes will help you feel the area within your body where this emotion seems to reside, the place where it feels the strongest. It may feel like a constriction or tightness. Often it is along the centerline of the body, in the stomach or lower abdomen, the heart area or the throat area.

Your willingness to experience this sensation for a few seconds, and to allow your breath to flow into the constricted area of the body, will help that sensation to relax and dissipate. Contrary to what you may have been told, or what you may have thought, experiencing this energy in the body does not increase the discomfort, it releases it. Being willing to feel the sensation in the body is the key.

Try it now and see for yourself.

You can do this Exercise many times each day.

If you don't understand the Exercise, or did not seem to gain anything from doing it, don't worry. We're going to cover this in a lot more detail in Exercise 3-B.

Please use your Notebook to record any ideas
or insights that you had.

3
Guilt and Blame: The Silent Assasins

When Julie first became ill, I experienced guilt. I blamed myself. Blame turned inward is experienced as guilt. Guilt and blame are silent assassins. They are not desirable emotions and are often accompanied by feelings of unease. They also can be responsible for emotions such as depression or anger.

If it continues long enough a disease might develop.

My guilt caused me to become angry and depressed. I wondered why I was singled out to experience the hell of Julie's mental illness. If you feel or have felt the same way, you are not alone. How can you not feel anger when a bomb like mental illness is dropped into your lap?

One of the prime sources of my personal guilt could be summarized in the question: "Why did I not recognize this as it was developing?"

Looking back, I realized that Julie began to slip away long before that bizarre morning on the bathroom floor. She began to see things as strictly black and white. Previously tolerant and broad-minded, she had cut off her relationship with her mother two years earlier. She said her mother just "didn't get her"—and it would be best for both of them if they stopped communicating. She similarly broke off her relationship with her son for about a year. Additionally, she stopped seeing and talking to several of her best friends.

Why did I not realize these were signs of someone struggling to make sense of her world?

Another source of guilt was that Julie's illness had indirectly led to the loss of my job. The company I had been with for almost 16 years was more than just an employer. The three owners were personal friends. Julie and I shared Thanksgivings with them; went on sailing and fishing trips together, and enjoyed a genuine, mutual friendship. They were continuously generous to us in many ways. But Julie began to mistrust them. She insisted they were cheating me.

Instead of seeing that her vision of them was distorted, I relied upon her instincts and acted in ways that ultimately led to my dismissal.

Before Julie became ill, I trusted her financial decisions. She processed her information intuitively and for many years was completely reliable. Even when I didn't understand the logic of some decision she was making, I relied upon her, because it had worked out in the past. Since she had always made decisions on this intuitive level, it did not occur to me to question her when her ideas no longer made sense. We had a large, personal investment that she was handling. When it failed, we lost our life savings. This placed even more pressure upon her.

Looking back at this combination of events, I concluded that I had much to feel guilty about. I felt as if I had been "asleep at the wheel" while she was slipping away. Why hadn't I seen the situation more clearly? There were enough signs to indicate that all was not well. Where was I during all of this?

But no matter how much I wish I could turn the clock back and make different decisions, her mental illness probably still would have occurred.

Do you ever wish you could go back in time, do things differently and create a different outcome? Unfortunately the process of wishing something did not happen does not create a different result. In many cases, rather than helping, it takes us further from our goal of recovering our balance and moving forward with our life again.

Anger, guilt, blame and shame are normal responses to negative occurrences. These need to be acknowledged. You might feel you no longer have these feelings. Or that you have dealt with them. This is natural. The tendency is often to assume that if we don't think about something, it no longer affects us. This logic suggests that if we just ignore a problem, it will go away.

Have you ever tried to ignore something to which you have a large emotional connection? It's a little like the story of everyone seeing that there is an elephant in the room, but at the same time pretending it is not there. The first step in getting the elephant *out* of the house is to acknowledge that we have an elephant *in* the house. Only then can we take steps to remove the elephant. Prior to acknowledging the elephant's presence, nothing much can be done.

In much the same way, once we recognize that we have feelings of guilt and blame, it becomes possible to begin to heal these destructive emotions. Part of this Guidebook's effectiveness lies in its ability to help uncover these "hidden emotions."

Using the Exercise below, we will now bring these feelings to the surface, so that they can be seen. By doing this, they become our allies rather than our tormentors. We will learn how to free the energy trapped in emotions of hopelessness, anger, guilt, blame, shame, resentment, and other negative feelings.

This Exercise is easy to do, highly effective, and it will make you feel better every time you do it.

Exercise 3-A: What Have I Said to Myself?

Please go to your Notebook now, while this information is fresh, and write your description of what you thought your part was in your loved one's mental illness. My story is based on the conditions I found myself in. Your story will be different.

If you have a child who was born with a mental illness, you might be telling yourself that you should have researched your family history—or that of your partner—more thoroughly. Perhaps you might secretly wish you had not experimented with drugs when you were in college. Do you think the recreational drugs might have caused this condition? Have you criticized yourself because you and your partner did not have medical tests performed before or after you conceived? You might wonder if everyone would have been better served if there had been an abortion.

The key to this Exercise is to censor nothing.

Please take a few minutes to write your description of what you thought your part was in this event. If there was something you think you should have known, write it down. If there was something you wished you had done or not done, said or not said, include it. If there were earlier signs something was wrong, or could possibly have been wrong, list them. Do not leave anything out, however painful it might be.

Any response you have regarding your role in your own situation has a reason for being there. Acknowledging it takes the power out of it. Compose your response as honestly and completely as you can. If you think of additional items later on, add them to the list.

Use these sample questions to get started:
- What have I said to myself about this situation?
- In what way do I feel responsible?
- What could I have done that might have prevented it, or might have lessened it?
- What do I wish I had known or not known that might have made a difference?
- What do I think about my role in all of this?

***Please go to your Notebook at this time
and complete this Exercise.***

The Mind Body Connection

For the next Exercise (which I will summarize at the end of this section) you will need to be aware of the connection between the mind and the body. All of the Exercises in this Guidebook are important, but this is one of the most important. We will refer back to it repeatedly for the remainder of this program.

Thoughts are flowing through our minds all the time. It is estimated that the average person has about 60,000 thoughts each day. (I was shocked when I first heard that number.)

Unfortunately, many thoughts are the same ones we had yesterday, and the day before that. Even thoughts that are not serving us, thoughts that make us feel unhappy, angry or depressed tend to repeat hour after hour, day after day, year after year. They make us feel bad today, and they will probably make us feel bad tomorrow.

In addition to thoughts continually flowing through our minds, feelings are continually flowing through our bodies. When I use the word feeling I am referring to a type of energy, a sensation within the body that can be experienced when we are quiet. Feelings can have a range—from intense to mild. One feeling is not better or worse than another; they are all just energy. Like all energy systems, feelings are most healthy when they are flowing. Consider a flowing river versus a stagnant lagoon. One is fresh, alive, and continually regenerating. The other is restricted and brackish, because it is not moving.

When we become quiet, feelings can be experienced as subtle sensations or vibrations somewhere in our body. They might be felt as a faint impulse, a gentle tingle, or possibly even a mild discomfort.

When thoughts and feelings join together, we have what is known as an emotion. The definition that I am using throughout this Guidebook is that an emotion is the linking of a sensation in the body with a thought in the mind. Through this process, a meaning or interpretation gets assigned to these feelings or sensations in the body. When this happens we say things like: "I feel angry, because my friend is not going to the movie with me," or "I feel happy, because I am going on vacation in two weeks." The mind always wants to assign a meaning to describe the feeling or sensation of energy in the body. This is just the way we are made.

By separating a thought from a feeling, however, we can begin to dismantle the strong energy that is contained within some of our dominant emotions. This is the purpose of this Exercise. We use a tool to break the connection—and as a result we gain a sense of freedom and empowerment that we did not have before. What we are going to learn with this Exercise is how to take the power out of strong emotions, so that they can begin to diminish—and eventually disappear altogether.

The technique is simple. We locate the feeling in our body, the place where the sensation seems to be the strongest. We seek its center, the place where the energy feels the most intense. Typically it will be around our heart, our throat, or somewhere in our abdomen, but it could be found anywhere in our body. It doesn't matter where the sensation resides, we just try to locate it.

If you have any difficulty locating it at first, just close your eyes and think of the situation you were writing about in the previous Exercise. Think about what you said *your role* was. Allow your attention to be drawn to that place in your body where there seems to be some sensation, or tension, or tightness, when you think about this issue. This is not difficult to do, so you do not need to try hard. See where your body seems to be screaming the loudest when you think—with your eyes closed—about this situation. This will be the area you seek.

This feeling in the body is separate from any thought you might be having. This feeling or sensation is located in the body, and thoughts are located in the mind. Experience the "body energy" rather than focusing on the "thought energy." The commentary that might be going on in your mind is unimportant for this Exercise. Stay present with the feeling in the body. It is just a sensation—possibly faint, possibly strong. Just continue to experience it. Allow your attention to experience the body energy, separate from any thought you might have about it.

Now breathe deeply into the place where you feel the sensation. We are using our imagination here. Obviously we are still breathing using our lungs and the other components of our respiratory system. But it is possible to feel as if we are breathing into a particular area of the body. Don't strain with this. Just know that it is easy and possible to feel the air going to this particular area and softening it.

It is possible that you will feel a sense of release at some point. This is what we are looking for, a bit of release or softening in some area of the body. This change might not seem like much to you, but this process allows the energy to dissipate—which is what we want to accomplish.

Take as much time with this as you like; a few moments or half an hour. There is no right amount of time for this step. You will know it is complete when you feel a slight release inside yourself. Another telltale sign is that your mind will quiet down around the issue in question. You might take in a sudden deep breath, almost like a sigh. You might even feel joy or peacefulness when this step is complete.

The final step is to try to feel love or appreciation for yourself—an opposite feeling from anger or resentment. If you have a spiritual background, you might feel the love and appreciation for yourself arising from your concept of God—or a divine being that you resonate with—or simply from the universe itself. You might feel this love arising from a grandparent, or even a pet—someone who you are certain has loved you. It is not important whom you associate this love with; it is only important that you experience it.

Now that you understand the concepts, let's complete Exercise 3-B. It is summarized for you on the next page.

Exercise 3-B: The Energy Release Process

1. Do you recall the situation you were writing about in Exercise 3-A; the situation just as it is, with all of the anger, disappointment, regret, hopelessness, blame, shame, guilt, or any other emotion you might feel. Now close your eyes and notice what's going on in your body. You will be drawn to some area of your body where the energy or sensation around these emotions feels the strongest. Breathe deeply into this area. Ignore any thought you might be having. Your attention should be on the sensation in your body, rather than with any thought in your mind. Relax into the energy, the sensation that you feel in your body. Can you allow your breath to soften this sensation? There is nothing to resist, and you do not need to try very hard. It is more of an allowing than a doing. When you feel a release or quieting of mental chatter, go to the next step (Step 2).

2. Feel love and appreciation extending to yourself from a divine source—or a grandparent, a pet, or anyone who you know loves you or has loved you. Feel it fully. Can you feel this love for you, while at the same time you are experiencing the sensation in your body? It is all just energy. Allow this feeling to permeate your entire body. Some people feel it as a brilliant, white, liquid light—filling them from head to toe. It might feel quite enlivening and joyful. You might have your own visual impression that accompanies this experience, or you might have no visual experience at all. Just be at ease with whatever happens.

3. When you feel complete, open your eyes and notice how you are feeling. Many people report feeling a little lighter and often a bit less worried.

Please use your Notebook to record any ideas
or insights that you might have had.

The Mind Body Connection Summary

If practiced regularly, this Exercise alone can provide great joy, freedom, and empowerment. It is simple, but very effective. Use it whenever you feel overwhelmed, unhappy, depressed, angry, or any other negative emotion. You can never suppress these emotions and have them disappear permanently, but this Exercise will cause them to diminish. Energy that was trapped in your body is now "freed up," and has the opportunity to be used in more beneficial and productive ways.

The key is your willingness to feel the energy in the body, the sensation in the body, as separate from any thought you have. Once you understand this concept and feel the results of this Exercise, you will be able to take the power out of any situation that you find troublesome or uncomfortable. Sometimes the effect is immediate. Sometimes it is gradual. But it always works.

After you have completed the Energy Release Exercise, take a break. Congratulate yourself for the work that you have done. It is a significant step toward regaining your joy, contentment and peace. If possible, go for a walk—even a short one around the block. Or take a hot bath. Or have a dessert that you love. Or put on your favorite music. Give yourself some form of reward for having entered into this dialogue which allows you to see, feel, and accept that you did nothing wrong.

Had you known earlier what you know now, possibly you would have chosen differently. But you did the best you could at the time. That is all any of us can do, and therefore you are not to blame.

Thank you for coming along on this journey.

Who Else Might Be Responsible?

We have now begun the process of absolving ourselves of any wrongdoing, and you have a practical tool (The Energy-Release Exercise) for dealing with these feelings whenever they return.

Now let's turn our attention to all of the "others" whom we might be holding responsible for this situation.

In the next Exercise, you will be asked to list all of those whom you feel could possibly be to blame. Just like in Exercise 3-A, when we were dealing with self-blame, the important thing is to be completely honest and to include everyone and everything. If you feel someone or something could be even slightly to blame, put them on the list. Don't leave out anyone.

I want to use a strong-but-fictitious example to illustrate a specific point. Let's say that someone in your family was injured in a car accident, and that this has resulted in a loved one having a permanent mental impairment. Let's also say that the driver who caused the accident was drunk, did not have a driver's license or insurance, and was in violation of his parole.

This is an extreme example; intense anger and blame would be an automatic initial response from all of us. Given the above description, and the fact that there was an accident that caused permanent harm, we could certainly blame the drunk driver— hold him responsible. We might also blame the legal system for not keeping him in prison or monitoring his parole more carefully. We might blame the bar down the road that continued to serve him drinks when he was already intoxicated. We might blame the driver's parents for not doing a better job of raising their son. We could blame the police for not noticing the drunken driver before he caused the accident. We might blame the alcohol industry for making products that cause people to lose their coordination and judgment. There might be many people for us to feel anger toward. Such anger would be understandable.

The above fictitious example illustrates how blame can easily become embedded in any life situation, particularly those events we do not like. When we start actively looking for anyone who could have been even remotely responsible, we might end up with quite a long list.

Exercise 3-C: Who Else Might Be Responsible?

To get you started thinking about all those who might belong on your "Prominent Suspects List," (those you blame) I suggest you consider professionals such as doctors, lawyers, or the police. (They were all sources of anger and frustration for me.)

Include any family members who might have contributed to the situation.

Have you experienced strong emotions around employers, the government, neighbors, friends, or enemies?

What about the mentally ill person? Does it seem sometimes that they are not trying hard enough, or cooperating enough?

Do not leave out the drug companies that have not yet found a permanent cure for many afflictions—and whose current treatments usually have unpleasant side effects.

And let's not forget the politicians who have repeatedly cut budgets for mental healthcare facilities and treatments.

If your feelings are overpowering when you do this Exercise don't worry, this is a great sign.

If you feel like crying, go ahead. You have every right to feel furious, sad, victimized, overwhelmed and hopeless. I felt every one of these emotions.

The purpose of this Exercise is to allow us to take the "high-voltage charge" out of these emotions. If you have a strong emotional reaction, this Exercise will help to dissipate that energy. So go ahead and list—and describe the involvement of—everyone who could possibly have had anything to do with this situation.

Repeat Exercise 3-B: The Energy Release Process

It is very important that when you bring up all of the unpleasantness, you then clear it with the Energy Release Process that you learned earlier in this chapter and repeat the Exercise. This clears the energy field, and will result in a feeling of release and increased contentment.

If the unpleasant feelings return at a later time, repeat the Energy Release Exercise. In many cases it takes only a few moments to do, and you will always feel better. Over time these negative emotions will diminish and eventually fade away completely.

Chapter 3—Summary

Congratulations! You have now completed another important step in reclaiming your power. By engaging in this process you will be better equipped to help your loved one. Remember, we need to save ourselves before we can assist others.

How do you feel? If you still feel a bit unsettled, that's normal. Take your time with this. This negative energy might have had a long incubation period.

If you feel a little more centered after these Exercises, then take a few moments to notice how much freer you feel—and how much more clearly you might be seeing the situation. Your physical surroundings might even appear to have greater sharpness, much like when we clean our glasses, and then everything we look at appears more focused. You might even be feeling more optimistic, possibly even happy inside. Go ahead and enjoy these feelings. You have created them, and you are learning how to take your power back from your circumstances so that it can be used in new ways, to create more of what you desire in life.

If you did not notice much, after doing this Exercise, do not become discouraged. We are going to be learning new ways of addressing these energy patterns as we move through this Guidebook. Many things in life do not produce the complete effect on the first try. The fact that you are even trying to gain new insight and relieve some of the stress is commendable.

In summary, whenever anything happens to us that we do not like, we tend to blame ourselves and others. Much of the strong emotion we feel around any challenging situation is due to the concepts of guilt and blame that we hold in our minds. But since guilt and blame are only mental concepts they can be altered using the techniques you are learning in this Guidebook.

Blame and guilt occur because we feel disappointed by the circumstances we find ourselves in. This is a natural response to any disruptive life event, and certainly a mental illness in our family would be high on anyone's list of a major life challenge.

If we are still angry many years later, however, it means we have not moved forward from our initial understanding. Blame and guilt maintained over a long period of time are not healthy—and they fuel the emotions of anger and depression. We must work through this idea of blame if we are to re-establish peace and happiness. It's not easy work, but it must be done. Being angry about some event long after it happened is not as satisfying as having a happy and productive life. And these conditions are mutually exclusive; choosing one automatically eliminates the other.

4

The Five Stages of Grief

Dr. Elisabeth Kübler-Ross, the great Swiss psychiatrist and author, identified what became known as the "Five Stages of Grief"—while she was working with terminally ill cancer patients. These categories—which she defined in the late 1960's—represent the feelings of terminally ill people.

Over time, many professionals began to apply her understanding to other difficult life events, such as a divorce, the loss of a job, a serious illness, or some other life challenge. The idea has now been expanded to include not only people facing their own life challenge (i.e. death, divorce, etc.), but also those who are supporting someone they love through *their life challenge*. Not only do we grieve our own impending death, but also the loss of those recently departed, or those getting ready to depart. It is therefore not a big stretch to include the mental illness of a family member in this category. Mental illness may represent a kind of death (of a personality)—and it is certainly a major life challenge.

The five stages of coping with dying were described by Elisabeth Kübler-Ross in her classic book *On Death and Dying* in 1969:

1. Denial and Isolation: "This is not happening to me."
2. Anger: "How dare God do this to me?"

3. Bargaining: "Just let me live to see my son graduate."
4. Depression: "I can't bear to face going through this, putting my family through this."
5. Acceptance: "I'm ready, I don't want to struggle anymore."

Kübler-Ross never intended these stages to be a "rigid framework" that applies to everyone who mourns or faces a difficult challenge. She supported the notion that each person's response will be unique. In her last book, before her death in 2004, she said of the five stages: "They were never meant to help tuck messy emotions into neat packages. They are responses to loss that many people have; but there is not a typical response to loss—just as there is no typical loss. Our grieving is as individual as our lives."

There also is no timetable for grieving. Your sense of loss and intermittent sadness may never go away completely; people experience the cycle of grief differently. Some find that within a few weeks or months, the interval between waves of distress lengthens. These people are able to feel peace, renewed hope, and more enjoyment in life. Others, however, may face years of relentless waves of grief. As Kübler-Ross said, it is an individual process.

I personally was stuck at the anger stage for several months. I asked myself over and over, "Why did this happen to Julie and me?" I was looking to blame someone, even myself, for this torturous event.

I found that the "Why Question" never produced anything useful. I was never able to get a satisfactory answer, and in retrospect, I think it caused a lot of additional confusion.

Eventually I began to frame the question into something more useful—"What should I do next about this?" or, "Who could I talk to about this latest development?" These types of questions engage the mind in a different way. When we use them, we begin to develop an openness that seeks a solution. We start looking forward, rather than continuing to look backward.

I realized that asking myself "Why?" over and over was not helpful, and was in fact complicating my situation. Altering this question was a turning point for me.

The next Exercise may help you discover where you are in the grief process. We will be working with a variety of strategies in the coming chapters to help you move through this process with greater ease and fluidity.

If after completing this Guidebook—including working through all of the Exercises—you still feel that you are stuck in a cycle of grief (and it is impacting your life in a significant way) you may want to seek additional help. If your feelings seem as strong and overwhelming as when the events first took place, I suggest that you consider a grief-support group, or the option of private therapy. At the very least, I suggest you consult with your family physician.

You also might want to consider contacting the National Alliance on Mental Illness (NAMI), which has chapters in many U.S. cities. This agency offers support for the families of the mentally ill, as well as support for the mentally ill themselves.

Exercise 4: Where am I on the Five Stages Chart?

Do you have an emotion from the list (denial, anger, bargaining, depression, and acceptance) that seems particularly dominant?

Have you experienced all of these emotions, in relation to a situation of mental illness, at one time or another?

Do you seem to move frequently between two or more stages?

Think about this for a few moments. Remember, there is no typical response, and no typical timetable; this is an individual process, and everyone goes through it differently. To even be able to admit to ourselves that we may be angry or depressed is a big step forward. It's all a part of the healing process.

Do you continue to ask yourself "Why"—over and over again? Has anything useful ever come of it? Have you ever received an answer that permanently put this question to rest?

The next time you are tempted to ask yourself that question, move to another strategy. Try asking: "What should my next step be?" or, "Who can I talk to in order to gain some additional insight?"

Questions such as these can move you forward, while the "Why Question" does not.

Please use your Notebook to record any ideas
or insights that you may have had.

Part II

Discovering the Strength Within to Survive, Heal and Transcend

5

Cutting Away the
Stigma of Mental Illness

I vividly remember the social worker who first uttered the words "bipolar" and "paranoid schizophrenia" to describe my wife. The social worker and I were in a hospital waiting room in Las Vegas; Julie had been admitted a few hours earlier.

The social worker was asking for my input, to confirm a diagnosis. "Mr. Jacobs, I am going to read some descriptions out of the Diagnostic and Statistical Manual of Mental Disorders. I want you to tell me which of these descriptions most closely resemble your wife's recent behavior."

Julie's medical evaluation—a blunt but accurate description of her behavior—hit me like a frigid winter wind. The description the social worker read was so accurate. How could something written in a book perfectly describe the bizarre experience I had witnessed?

At the time, I did not know anything about mental illness. I was totally unprepared. I felt all alone. I even felt unstable myself, as I tried to process this event. I referred to this in Chapter Two as feeling like I was living in "No Man's Land."

Given this feeling of isolation and bafflement, it would have been an excellent idea to contact my family and friends in order to gain their support. But I did exactly the opposite; except for one trusted friend, I kept this entire situation to myself for several weeks.

Why, in this most troubled time of my life, did I behave this way? I was not even aware of my avoidance of family and friends until the one friend in whom I had confided, a psychologist, said to me: "You need to let your family and friends know about this. You're going to need a lot of support to get through this. You can't do this on your own."

After we spoke, and as I digested her comment, I realized that I didn't *want* to let anyone know. I felt embarrassed. It was as though Julie and I had done something wrong.

Why would I feel this way? Would I have felt this way if Julie had developed a serious physical illness, rather than a mental illness? I doubt it.

In retrospect, this avoidance was very interesting. In analyzing it, I discovered that even though we consider ourselves to be out of the Dark Ages—and we no longer lock people up in horrible places on the outskirts of town—we still have misperceptions, fears, and embarrassments about mental illness. Maybe we grew up hearing about Aunt Bertha—whom no one would talk about. Or maybe we harbor fears that if the security ever broke down at "one of those places," we would be in immediate danger.

Books and movies we have seen certainly do not help. It has been a source of entertainment to look at the bizarre workings of the human psyche. Our culture retains an enormous collective fear of mental illness. Consequently we treat mental illness differently than physical illness. And of course, it is different.

When someone develops a respiratory disease, a heart disease, or loses the use of an arm or leg they are still basically the same person. They can consult with medical experts, research the illness on their own, analyze options, discuss it with their family and friends, and eventually make a decision regarding their treatment. They may decide to have treatment A, or treatment B, or forgo treatment altogether. Even the decision not to treat an ailment is a decision based on the information they possess and what they think will be best.

When mental illness is involved, however, the primary decision maker may not be able to make decisions, or at least not good ones. It is quite different to consult with someone on how they plan to treat their heart-disease diagnosis, versus consulting with that same person about how they intend to treat their schizophrenia diagnosis.

In the case of Julie and myself, I needed support from my family and friends right from the beginning. But I was in denial. This was not healthy, but I didn't know it. So I kept silent, which put even more pressure on me.

Only after I started to tell people what happened did the pressure decrease.

It was awkward with some friends and family. I had to give Julie's son some disturbing news about his mother. That was not easy. It was about five months after he and I spoke that he finally encountered Julie's condition. It was during one of her manic and delusional episodes, that he saw firsthand what this illness looked like.

After that encounter, he told me he and his wife had wondered if there was *something wrong with me*—or with *my perception* of the situation—when I first explained Julie's illness. They did not want to believe that Julie was ill.

One of Julie's best friends, Tina, had a similar response. Julie spoke to Tina multiple times, and told her I was having an affair and that I was planning on "running off" with my new lover. When I finally spoke to Tina, several months later, I told her about Julie's illness. Tina's initial thought was that I had concocted an outrageous story about Julie in order to "cover up" for my own bad behavior.

My brother's initial response was to inform me that he had never liked Julie, and that she was not a good marriage partner for me.

These varied types of reaction are difficult to deal with when you already are feeling overwhelmed by your circumstances. Could it be that our fear of the misperception and distortion from our family and friends complicates our willingness to share information in the first place?

Elizabeth, the mother of a 20-year-old boy with severe depression, told me that her main concern had been to protect her son from other children—or even family members—who might mock him. She did not even want to share her son's diagnosis with her husband. She feared that her husband would talk to his mother, and then within hours every member of the family would be calling, saying: "How is Jeremy? I understand he has some mental problems?"

Sally, a woman married to a bi-polar man for eight years, never shared information about her husband's illness with her own mother. Only after her marriage ended did Sally tell her mother about her husband's condition. Sally might have benefitted from her mother's love, support, and understanding during those eight long years. But she never shared the information that would have gained such support.

I do not suggest that you abandon all discretion and tell everyone you know about sensitive situations. In some cases it could do more harm than good. But I suggest that you consider adding close, trusted friends and relatives to your support team.

It is possible you will encounter some confusion or distress if you include others, but you need to allow others to have their responses. They will arrive at their own understanding in their own time.

Keep in mind that they, too, might be losing the friend, brother, mother, or daughter that they have always known. This requires an adjustment on everyone's part.

Disclosure may be uncomfortable, but you, as the primary caregiver, need the support of these people. You cannot do it alone. And eventually (in my experience) friends and family members want to be helpful. They will adjust to the situation, regardless of their initial response.

Another factor contributing to our unwillingness to share this information is our culture. Many of us may feel that asking for help is a weakness. This can be particularly true for men. Certainly I felt that way. It may have been one reason that I was hesitant to involve my family and friends when Julie became ill.

The reality, however, is we all need help from time to time; it has nothing to do with being a strong person, or a self-sufficient person. There is a limit to everyone's strength and capabilities. Therefore it is desirable that we help one another when situations arise that require support. The corollary is that people need to accept support from others in times of need.

It is a gift we have as humans to be able to both give support, and receive it.

Exercise 5-A: Why didn't I Share with Others?

Have any of these factors caused a delay in seeking help?

- Embarrassment that this was happening

- Denial there was even a problem

- Procrastination – "I'll do it tomorrow"

- Hoping it might resolve itself

- Wondering what good it could possibly do to have others involved

- Feeling guilty about the entire situation

- Feeling that you possibly caused the problem— it was your fault

- Feeling too depressed to do much of anything

- Thinking that no one could help anyway

- Not wanting to worry friends and family members

- Desiring to protect your (son, wife, mother, etc.) from bullying or possible embarrassment

- Not wanting to be obligated to provide endless updates to everyone

- Not considering your own needs—all the attention should go to the ill family member.

- Something not listed above, but nevertheless influential. If you are uncertain what this might be, close your eyes and ask this question silently to yourself: "Why didn't I share this with more people?" Whatever answer you receive, see if it "makes sense" when you try to understand your reluctance to share.

Based upon the above descriptions, go to your Notebook and write down anything that might be keeping you from enlisting additional support.

Please use your Notebook to record any ideas or insights that you may have had.

Exercise 5-B: People Who are Supporting You (or could possibly Support You)

Everyone requires help from time to time, and we all can be a source of help to others. With this in mind, go to your Notebook and list all the people who support you now—or could in the future. These might be family members, friends, possible financial supporters, family physician, and other health-care professionals. The list also might include therapists, counselors, ministers or chaplains, mental health support groups such as NAMI (National Alliance on Mental Illness), or other individuals or groups.

What I have presented is not a comprehensive list; it's just designed to get you started. Consider creating three lists:

A. Those who are currently supporting me

B. Those who might be capable of supporting me

C. A form of support that I need, but I presently do not know the person or organization that might provide it

We will deal with the concept from "List C" more fully later in this book. For now, the simple act of identifying something we need, with no consideration as to how we might fulfill the need, opens us to new opportunities. Just holding it in our mind as a possibility, with no thought as to how it might happen is the key. If you have such a need, place it on this list.

Please use your Notebook to record any ideas or insights that you may have had.

68

Chapter 5—Summary

Mental illness in our family is a major life challenge. As such, it requires significant support from others—both professional support and support from family and friends. But because of the stigma of mental illness, many people do not enlist all the support that is available to them.

If you feel the need to repeat the Energy Release Exercise found in Chapter Three, please do so. Feel free to use it whenever you experience discomfort, or when you feel resistant to any idea that is being presented. This is the reason it was provided early in the book.

Negative emotional energy literally becomes trapped in our minds and bodies. It creates pain, confusion, poor health, and feeds upon itself in an expanding downward spiral. The process described in the Energy Release Exercise breaks this cycle, and allows the energy to be freed; the energy can then be used creatively. Think of it as "energy recycling." We take something that is no longer valuable—like something we have placed in the garbage—and recycle it into something useful. This tool alone can be a major source of support for you.

We are now ready to understand one of the most interesting concepts in the Guidebook.

6

Challenging the Interpretation of the Illness

Since prehistory, human beings have used stories to help explain who they are and how they function in this complex experience we call life. Long before anything was written, cultures from all over the world told their stories. Stories were one way to perpetuate accumulated knowledge.

Such stories might become distorted and exaggerated as they were retold through the generations, but the essence of the event was passed on for the benefit of everyone. Stories help us to learn, to remember, to connect with the past. They also provide a framework which makes us feel that we belong and that we are safe.

Families have their own unique stories. Can you remember your parents telling you about a family event that happened years earlier? If you are like me, family stories were told so often that every family member could recite them. To tell a story is a basic function of being human—much like eating, sleeping, or dreaming. If you are alive, you tell stories—both to yourself and to others.

But a question needs to be asked: "How many of our stories are really true?" For instance, if the police ask five people who witnessed a car accident what they saw, there might be five different versions of the incident. Psychologists know that—depending upon how and where we were raised—events impact us differently. Even within the same family, different interpretations of an event by different family members are normal. This means the stories that we tell ourselves over and over have two separate components. The first is what happened—just the facts. And the second is our interpretation of those facts—what we say those facts mean.

Let's look at the above example of the car accident in a little more detail. What happened is that two cars collided. That is the basic fact, and everyone agrees. How we might interpret that fact, however, might depend upon many variables. What was our point of reference? Were we traveling in one of the cars involved? In an adjacent car? In a car behind the cars involved in the accident? Were we standing on a bridge above the accident? Were we looking at the cars before the accident occurred, or did we only turn to look once we heard the crash?

Do we have one or more prejudices that influence our judgment? Age, for instance, or race, or some other physical characteristic? Do we think no one should drive over 50 mph under any circumstance? Have we had one or more accidents ourselves? All of this and more is what influences our interpretation of the event.

Two separate components—the facts, and our interpretation of the facts—merge into a single understanding. And this combination is the story that we tell to ourselves and others.

Once we understand this concept, we can provide ourselves with mental and emotional freedom—freedom that did not previously exist. Let's continue with this premise to understand how and why it works.

Everyone Is Right about His or Her Story

I want to introduce a potent concept, one that can assist you in any situation you will ever encounter. As far as your story goes, you get to be right. But so does everyone else, with regard to their story. We are all correct in what we say about anything, because it is our story.

In addition to the facts, the story is based upon many other things—such as our perceptions, interpretations, past experiences. We are also influenced by our family, cultural and religious backgrounds. All of these influences, and more, form a "filter" through which we see every event.

To a child looking through a pair of plastic glasses with green lenses, everything appears green. If the child looks through a pair of blue lenses, the same scene appears to be blue. So the real question is not whether or not we are right; everyone gets to be right from their point of view. The real question is: "What is it we are choosing to be right about?" What story are we telling ourselves, over and over, about our circumstances, our past, our hopes and our fears?

This concept may take some time to digest. That's fine. Just continue to breathe and try to stay open to this new possibility.

Let me give you an example to help clarify this concept. Let's say you stop for breakfast one morning at a coffee shop you have not been to before. You sit at the counter and notice that no one is getting very good service. It takes the waitress several minutes to take your order, and several more minutes to get your coffee. She is very inattentive, not only to you but to the other customers. In addition to the bad service, you notice she spends time talking to another waitress rather than taking care of her customers.

When the cook has finished preparing your meal, it sits under the warming lights for several minutes before she breaks off her conversation to bring your food to you. After waiting for your bill for ten additional minutes, you are quite annoyed. You have been there for forty-five minutes, and the complete lack of service took all the enjoyment out of the experience.

Now take a moment to reflect on how much of a tip you would leave, how much tip you think would be appropriate, based upon the above description. Let's say the breakfast cost eight dollars. What is your tip going to be?

Now let's continue with this scenario. You are so irritated with this waitress that you ask to speak to the manager, and you explain to her what has happened. The manager says she is sorry for the inconvenience, takes your bill and says there will be no charge. Then she lets you in on a little secret.

"Lucy is my best waitress and consistently receives the most tips of any of my employees. Her young son was hit by a car last night and is in critical care. Lucy spent the entire night at the hospital, and only asked to come in this morning to try to get her mind off of the accident. I am sorry you had such poor service this morning."

Does this new information change your perspective regarding the lack of service? Do you now feel compassion for someone who is having a major life challenge? If you had the chance, would you like to say something kind to the waitress? Knowing what you know now, would you like to leave her a tip despite the poor service? Would you possibly even say a silent prayer for her and her child? Can you see how your perspective—your story—of this simple event changed as new information was added?

Here is the most interesting part of this example. We rarely have all the information necessary to make conclusive, absolute judgments. Nonetheless, we still have our opinions and stories about each situation. It is part of being human; we all have opinions and stories. But for every one of us, much of what we think and say is not 100 percent accurate—because we rarely know all there is to know about any given incident.

A person whose son had a mental illness previewed this book and asked: "What is the bottom line of this concept? Is it comfort with uncertainty?"

It is difficult to create a sense of comfort when we have a situation we do not want. We may even feel guilty because we feel healthy ourselves, while our loved one is in harm's way. But it is possible to suspend, at least partially, some of the anxiety and worry with the knowledge that "our story about it" is not strictly accurate; it contains some interpretation. With this understanding we are now ready to take the next step.

What If We Could Rewrite Our Story

Part of the reason we feel so uncomfortable with many of our life situations is that we have told ourselves a story about what has happened. And after a while, this story seems so real that nothing can change our mind about it.

But with any situation, there are certain facts which occurred—and facts as such have neither emotion nor meaning associated with them. There is also, however, interpretation of these facts by our mind. And interpretations vary from person to person, based upon family background, culture, religion, experiences, expectations, and other factors.

Just like the children with the colored glasses, the "filter" we look through influences what facts mean to us. Facts, and our interpretation of them, usually are not experienced as separate from one another. The facts and the interpretations form a composite that becomes "our story" of the event.

The following Exercise will help you separate the two components of the story you have around mental illness in your family. Please go to your Notebook now and complete the two parts to Exercise 6 below. You are starting to gain momentum, and you will feel better once you free the energy contained in your story of mental illness.

Exercise 6: Rewriting Your Story (Part One)

There are two parts to this Exercise. It will work best if you complete Part One, wait a day or two, and then do Part Two. If you have a big emotional response completing Part One, stop and do the Energy Release Exercise from Chapter Three to clear the emotional charge.

Complete Part Two when you feel more settled.

If you feel like crying, go ahead. You have every right to feel that way. It might be a welcome opportunity to free suppressed emotional energy.

The first part of this Exercise is to write your story with all of the emotion and detail you can muster. Make it big and bold—as if it were going to be sold as a screenplay, and made into a movie. Make it as descriptive as possible, and fill it with all the passion you have. You can work on this during multiple sessions if you desire, but do not skip over this. I am confident you will feel better after you complete the two parts of this Exercise.

***Please go to your Notebook now and
complete this part of the Exercise.***

Repeat Exercise 3-B: *Energy Release*

After writing the first part of this story with all the emotion, use the Energy Release Exercise located in Chapter Three to smooth out any unsettled feelings. It will help bring you back to a more centered place.

Do not become discouraged if the Exercise offers only some relief, and after completion the issue still has a "charge" to it. Some of those emotions may have been sitting there a long time. In some cases this Exercise may need to be repeated multiple times until the "emotional charge" is fully depleted.

This Exercise helps to release the judgments that are keeping the energy "stuck." Such judgments are often the root cause of our discomfort. When we are willing to simply experience the sensation in the body, without paying attention to what the mind may be saying about it, we are on our way to recovering our balance and power.

Exercise 6: Rewriting Your Story (Part Two)

Once you have completed Part One of this Exercise, write your story again, only this time with no emotion whatsoever. Write it with just the facts. Do you remember the car accident example at the beginning of this chapter? The only fact in that example was that two cars collided with each other.

When I first completed the two parts of this Exercise—writing the story of mental illness in my own family—I had about five pages of handwritten detail for Part One, and only three sentences for Part Two!

The facts from your story may not be quite so brief, but I am certain that you get the idea.

Proceed as though you were literally a fly on the wall, and your assignment is to report only the facts—devoid of opinion, beliefs, judgments, personal preferences, understanding or explanations. You are an independent observer who has no real interest in the story—no emotion or involvement whatsoever. Can you do this as a completely detached observer? Do it now. This will be more useful than you expect.

Please go to your Notebook now and
complete this Exercise.

Chapter 6—Summary

You should now see there are at least two interpretations of the same circumstance:

The story with just the facts contains the essence of the event, stripped of all the emotion, preferences and judgments.

The story with all the emotion and detail melded in is what we have thought and said about these facts.

This second story is our interpretation of the event; it is influenced by our prejudices, our family and cultural conditioning, etc. *Interpretation is a major cause of our suffering concerning any situation.* What we have said in our story creates the suffering. Un-interpreted facts—facts without all the filtering (the "should haves" and "could haves")—are not so painful.

There is an old adage, "What we resist persists." This means the things in life we wish were not there, we think should be different, or we have strong feelings and judgments about, will always be with us.

Developing an ability to separate the facts from the story can have a significant influence in resolving any disruptive life event. It works even for persistent difficulties that may have been with us for years. Without this insight, or some other method of gaining a new perspective, situations tend to stay the same—even when we attempt to change them.

Have you ever known someone who gets a divorce, only to find the next relationship contains many of the same problems as the previous marriage? Maybe you know someone who gets a new job, then discovers that the new position or new boss has many of the same qualities as the previous job.

The way to move beyond any circumstance in life is to first accept that it is as it is. If we do this, then new energy, new ideas, new possibilities have the opportunity to enter our lives.

I am not suggesting that we should pretend we no longer have personal preferences. Of course we prefer health to sickness, peacefulness to agitation, wealth to poverty. The key is to stop pushing against what is currently in our life.

If we stand in judgment of everyone and everything, and believe that because we interpret things in a particular way, everyone else should share our point of view, we will never be happy. If we judge life to be wrong, because it does not happen according to our preferences, we will never find contentment. For any situation in life the only sensible choice is to leave it, change it or accept it. Resistance is futile and rarely leads to happiness.

7
Discovering the Wisdom Within

Eckhart Tolle, author and visionary, in the introduction to his book, *The Power of Now*, tells of a beggar sitting on an old box and begging for coins. He asks a stranger for some change, and the stranger replies that he has nothing to give. The stranger then asks what the beggar is sitting on.

"Just an old box I have been sitting on for years," replies the beggar.

The story goes on to reveal that the beggar has been sitting on a box of gold all those years—begging because he did not realize what was inside his own box.

It is a beautiful allegory about the human condition. Most of us do not know what is within us. We feel the full weight of our difficulties, without being able to access the powerful energy that resides within our own mind.

This chapter's Exercise will help you discover what is within you, and how it can help alleviate any difficulty in life.

Exercise 7-A: The Art of Breathing: A Simple Meditation

Do you realize how amazing it is to be able to breathe freely? Possibly some of you cannot do this, and I would bet you would give just about anything to have this ability returned. For an average adult, we are breathing in and out approximately eight million times a year. Most of us are completely unaware of any effort to accomplish this. Isn't that a miracle?

In this Exercise we will use our breath to settle our mind and body, and through this process we will begin to discover what is within us. Please read the instructions once or twice, then close your eyes and enjoy the experience.

1. Find a comfortable, quiet place where you will not be disturbed for a few minutes. It will be best if you are sitting up comfortably with your back fairly straight rather that in a reclined position. Do not strain with this however. If you have difficulty sitting up straight, or need to be leaning back slightly, that is fine.

2. Close your eyes and become aware of your breath. The simple in and out of the breath is a phenomenon to be grateful for. Remember, not everyone has the ability to breathe easily. If you can breathe unencumbered, it is a blessing and it is possible to feel grateful for this ability. See if you can feel your diaphragm expanding and contracting rather than your chest. The expansion of the diaphragm is what makes our abdomen swell and subside.

3. Now go more deeply into the experience of your breath. You might become aware of the air moving in and out of your nostrils. Just notice the sensation. You might notice how your diaphragm rises with each inhalation and falls with each exhalation. Allow your attention to be with this most simple and natural process of breathing. We are not trying to notice anything in particular. We are just content to observe our breathing process. Whatever we experience is perfect.

4. If your mind wanders, return to your breathing. It is as simple as that. Regardless of how often the mind goes off to something else, bring yourself back easily to the breath. If you hear a car passing in the street, easily come back to the breath. Do not strain in any way. This is the easiest thing you have ever done. Despite the mind's tendency to go to something else, when we become aware of it, we gently return to our breath.

If we become absorbed in a thought, we really have no choice—the mind is thinking about something else. When we become aware, however, that we are thinking a thought instead of following our breath, we gently bring our attention back to the breath.

Do this breathing meditation for 15-20 minutes if you are able. You may feel at some point that you are witnessing your breathing—as if you are somehow separate from the person doing the breathing. It might even feel like you are being "breathed through."

You might feel that time passed quickly, and the Exercise is over before you knew it. You might feel that time passed slowly, and the Exercise seemed to take forever. You might have many thoughts, or very few.

All such experiences are fine. This Exercise is a form of meditation, and meditations are not all the same. Nor should you try to make them so.

Meditation has been used for thousands of years, and has gained mainstream credibility as an enormous boon to health.

If you are unable to do this Exercise for the recommended 15-20 minutes, then do it for 5-10 minutes. As you become more comfortable—and begin to experience the resulting peacefulness and clarity—expand your timeframe.

Do this every day—twice a day if you are able. This is a very simple and easy style of meditation that allows your mind to quiet, and your body to become energized. With a little practice you will find this an indispensable tool to regain balance, energy and your sense of well being.

If you have a comment for your Notebook
after this Exercise, please record it.

Exercise 7-B: The Art of Breathing: A Second Style of Meditation

Some of you may prefer the above meditation style, while others may prefer an alternative style. But please try the meditation style explained in 7-A a few times before you do this second style. This will allow you the ability to compare the two, and you can then decide which method you prefer.

This second style is called the Soham meditation or So Hum meditation. It is basically the same as the breathing meditation, with the following addition. When we inhale we mentally think the sound Sooooo, and when we exhale we mentally think the sound Hummmmm. These are sounds that your body makes when it is breathing—air moving in and out. These sounds may be familiar; you have been hearing them since birth.

Just relax and take it easy.

As in Exercise 7-A, if a thought comes, or if the mind is distracted by a noise, come back easily and effortlessly to your breath and the sound So Hum.

Enjoy!

*If you have a comment for your Notebook
after this Exercise, please record it.*

Chapter 7—Summary

Some of you will have a fantastic experience with this Breathing Exercise, some a slightly restful experience, and a few of you might feel that nothing happened. Whatever you experienced is fine. The results of meditation—where we begin to settle deeper and deeper into our own nature—will increase with practice.

I recommend that you do this Breathing Exercise every day—for about 15-20 minutes—for four weeks. This will provide you with an adequate evaluation period. If you become comfortable with meditation, there is a good chance you will do it for the rest of your life. (I have practiced meditation for more than 35 years, and consider it to be highly beneficial for health, happiness, and overall well-being.)

It is also beneficial to be able to meditate "on demand"—in other words whenever you wish to reconnect with this peaceful, joyful, contented feeling. It is always there, and always available. The only variable is our interest and willingness to connect with it. This is a significant treasure; I hope you will use it often.

In summary, we all have within us capabilities that we do not appreciate. One way these capabilities become obvious is through adversity. We do not look for adversity, but if you have found this Guidebook, you probably have had significant adversity. I can tell you with certainty that I am a stronger, more capable, and more balanced person than I have ever been. Did adversity help to bring this out of me? I believe that it did.

There was gold within the situation—and within me—that I had not previously recognized. Adversity helped me look harder and search deeper to discover more of what was already there.

The great American poet, Ralph Waldo Emerson summarized this beautifully: "What lies behind us and what lies before us are small matters compared to what lies within us."

Spend a little time each day bringing what is within you out into the world, and watch what happens!

8
Creating Your Personal Safety Zone

Julie and I had a Jack Russell Terrier—named Merlin—before and during Julie's illness. When Merlin was feeling confident, he seemed fearless. During the years we lived in California, there was a beach open to both dogs and horses. We usually took Merlin for a long walk most afternoons. Leashes were not required, so it was a chance for him to frolic with other dogs, chase the rolling waves, or play catch with a tennis ball or Frisbee.

What Merlin enjoyed most, however, was chasing galloping horses. Not a behavior we encouraged or desired, but we had a hard time controlling it. Sometimes Merlin would see, hear, or smell a horse before we could get him leashed. Then off he would go.

It was frightening to see Merlin running full speed between the legs of galloping horses— barking as loudly as he could. He was barking out of excitement. He was having a great time. He felt safe, confident, and in his element. We, on the other hand, felt fear. What if Merlin stumbled? What if the horse stumbled? What if the rider halted suddenly? What if the horse kicked him?

He was not, however, always full of courage and bravado. When we moved to Reno, we lived in the mountains, near a ski area. Periodically, during the winter months, the resorts would blast certain areas of snowpack with explosives—to prevent avalanches. The sounds of these explosions were not loud, because we lived several miles away.

Merlin, however, thought the end of the world was at hand. As soon as he heard an explosion, he began to shake, and yawn (his body's cry for more oxygen). He would continue this behavior until about an hour after the blasting stopped. Then he would have diarrhea and be lethargic for two days.

Was Merlin safe running with the horses? I don't know. It looked dangerous to me, but he never got hurt. He chased horses perhaps 50 times over a seven-year period. Based upon the outcome, I believe he was safe—even though it didn't appear that way.

Was he in danger during the anti-avalanche blasting? No, he was absolutely safe. It was miles away. But he didn't know that he was safe; he was certain that he was in danger. His mind, body, and emotions supported his belief that he was in danger. His physical reactions, therefore, were an accurate reflection of what he believed—even though what he believed was not true.

Can you see where I am going with this example? We have the capacity to feel safe in situations where others would not feel safe. We also have the capacity to feel unsafe simply because in our minds we are unsafe.

I have been a motorcyclist for 50 years. I feel safe riding through the mountains at 60-70 miles per hour. Many of you would not enjoy that experience. But I felt unsafe jumping out of an airplane with a parachute; some individuals feel totally safe doing it.

When we feel safe, we are relaxed and open to new information. We breathe deeply and enjoy our experience.

When we are afraid, we become tense. We tend to rely upon ideas or information we already have, rather than being open to new information or ideas. Our breathing becomes shallow, and usually we do not have a good time.

It is our perception of an event—rather than the actual event—that triggers a feeling of calmness or anxiety. What we think that an event means is what triggers our reaction—and our subsequent experience.

During the 10 years that I was married to Julie, I felt completely safe in our relationship. I was never worried about anything when I was with her—until an unexpected event called mental illness occurred.

At one point, after she became ill, Julie ran away to Santa Barbara for four months. I felt very vulnerable and unsafe during that time. Much of my anxiety came from my assumption that she was unsafe. I didn't know how she was taking care of herself, so sometimes I imagined the worst. Apparently she was safe, because nothing really bad happened to her.

A related example is a study done years ago. It tracked people's anxiety about possible stress-inducing life events that they were facing. The study followed up with the participants at a later date, to determine if what they had worried about had occurred.

Ninety percent of the things the participants worried about never happened at all. Of the remaining 10 percent, only two percent were as bad as anticipated.

This means that most times, only two percent of the things we feel anxious about will be as bad as we expect. To put it another way, 98 percent of the time, we worry too much. Most things we worry about never happen. What great news!

The purpose of this chapter is to make you reconsider your tendency to label events with absolute certainty. What I'd like you to do is be more objective when your mind forms an immediate opinion about something—particularly if it relates to safety. What you are forming is an idea or opinion, rather than an absolute value. And as we have seen, many of our judgments, ideas and opinions are not really accurate. We never know everything that there is to know about any situation. Therefore we cannot form ideas or opinions with absolute certainty.

With this in mind, we can allow a little of the wonder and mystery to creep back in to our lives. You had the ability to do this as a child; we all did. That ability still exists, but it's outside the bounds of your rational, thinking mind. If you can suspend immediate judgments and opinions—even for a short while—a new possibility just might sneak in.

Exercise 8: Creating Your Personal Safety Zone

What makes you feel safe? Have you always felt this way? Have relationships, possessions, situations or circumstances ever created ultimate safety for you? Do you think that they ever could?

If you believe that they have, then what do you think will happen if these relationships or circumstances change or go away? Will you then be unsafe?

On the flip side, what makes you feel unsafe now? What made you feel unsafe in the past? Has there ever been a time when you felt differently about the concept of safety? What about when you were a child? Did you have different attitudes and understandings then? Where did these ideas, attitudes and opinions come from? Were they derived from parents, teachers, siblings, friends, news media, movies, books?

Is it possible to expand your idea of safety? If something occurred that made you feel unsafe, right now, would you be able to deal with it?

What about things that represent safety to you? If an event did not happen exactly as you expected, would you be able to work around the situation?

Do you think you could increase your sense of contentment and freedom if you re-evaluated your personal notion of safety?

Write down answers to some of the questions above—as well as any other ideas you may have concerning the topic of safety.

Be easy on yourself. Remember that each of us views the world through a filter. And we developed that filter over time—years, decades, our lifetime. The filter is based upon thousands of experiences—some that we had personally, some that we only heard or read about.

It's time to start poking some holes in our notion of safety—a little here, a little there. Our perspective is not as real as we believe it to be. We can literally dismantle parts of it and replace those old and outmoded notions with ideas and concepts we find more useful.

Record in your Notebook any thoughts or insights you have about this subject.

9

Negotiating the Legal Quagmire

In September, 2005, I returned to Santa Barbara, California—a place Julie and I called home for more than nine years. She had run away from our home in Reno and retreated to a locale where she felt comfortable. I knew that Julie was living there because her credit card bills still came to our Reno home.

During this portion of Julie's illness, she accumulated approximately $100,000 in credit card debt. She lived in hotels and spent money lavishly. Such behavior is a trait of bipolar disorder.

I contacted the credit card companies and informed them of the situation, but I could not cancel the cards; they were in her name. The fact that Julie was mentally ill was irrelevant. Because Julie and I were married, I was liable for the debt—even though I could not stop the charges. This was a monstrous dilemma and added greatly to my stress level.

I began to speculate about what might snap Julie out of her delusional state of mind. I decided that if she were to encounter her son unexpectedly, it might help. (Julie had been married previously and had a grown son, John, a daughter-in-law, and two grandchildren.)

I contacted John and we worked out arrangements to meet in Santa Barbara to find Julie. We each rented a car and started cruising the streets. We checked restaurants that Julie had visited (based upon credit receipts), went to hotels where she had stayed, and checked places that Julie and I had frequented when we previously lived in Santa Barbara.

On the second day, John saw Julie at a hamburger stand near our previous home. He called me on my cell phone. "Steve, I have found her. She's at the Tinkers hamburger stand. I saw her walk in seconds ago. I'm certain it's her."

I decided to let John handle the encounter with Julie. Since her initial break with reality—about five months earlier—my presence typically made her suspicious and agitated.

"Fabulous, John," I said. "But approach her carefully. Try not to startle her. She's not the same as you remember her."

I drove to Tinkers and parked on a hill above the restaurant. I could see Julie's car, but that was all. I was so excited I could hardly control myself. I had not seen or heard from my wife in more than three months. To know she was still alive was a relief.

Could this be a turning point in her recovery? Would John—her own flesh and blood—be able to reach Julie? Help her? Anticipation and hopefulness raced through my entire being.

John told me later that he approached with the words: "Hi Mom. How are you?"

That did surprise her, he told me afterward. She asked him what he was doing in Santa Barbara. She became wary. Soon after John's approach, Julie spoke to a policeman who was in the restaurant having lunch: "Officer, this man is bothering me."

John—surprised and dismayed—took a family photo from his wallet and handed it to the officer. He explained that nothing inappropriate was going on, this was his mother. Julie was in the photo, along with John, his wife, and their two small children.

After glancing at the photo, the policeman turned to Julie and said: "Do you want to be with this man?"

"No," Julie responded. "I don't know him. He's bothering me."

The policeman then instructed John to stay away from Julie because he was violating the law.

John left the restaurant, flabbergasted by this rapid and unexpected turn of events. He called me and told me the news.

We followed Julie from the restaurant after this event and discovered where she was living. The next morning we sat outside her hotel. We were once again in separate cars; we didn't want her to slip away. We spoke on our cell phones, coordinating tactics. It might have been a fun game of cops and robbers, if the situation had not been so heartbreaking.

As we waited, John became excited and optimistic: "Steve, I know I can reach her. I'm going to knock on her door and see if I can just talk to her for a few minutes. I think I can persuade her to go back to the hospital. It's the only thing that has helped her in the past."

I was not in favor of John's plan. "John, I think she'll only get more upset. I don't think she'll speak to you. I think it will turn out just like yesterday."

I suggested that we strategize more. "Maybe I should call the mental hospital, John, and see if they have any ideas."

"Steve, I have to do this," John said. "My mom needs my help! I'll call you after I talk to her."

Thirty minutes later, John and I were speaking with another policeman. After knocking on her hotel room door, John said to Julie: "Mom, can I just talk to you for a few minutes. I'm not going to hurt you." Julie slammed the door and called the police.

This time the policeman was very firm with John. The officer knew about yesterday's incident at the hamburger stand.

He told John that he had to stay away from Julie; if there was one more incident, John would be arrested.

I tried to intercede and explained to the policeman that I had become accustomed to Julie's condition over a five-month period, but John was seeing his mother's mental state for the first time.

The policeman then gave us a clear summary of mental illness and the law: "It's not against the law to be crazy."

That may seem like a very stark and politically incorrect statement, but it clarified for me my struggle over the previous five months. I had been trying to get someone in authority to see that Julie needed help, and to support me in obtaining that help for her. I now understood why it could not happen. She was not breaking any law. From a legal perspective, any interference by her family was viewed as harassment—and subject to legal punishment.

How did this convoluted thinking arise, that a mentally ill person in the United States cannot receive the help they need unless strict—sometimes improbable—conditions exist.

If we look at the history of mental health care in the U.S., we find that there were abuses. In decades past, for example, if someone in a family was unhappy that Aunt Bertha became a Lutheran, after being raised a Catholic, they might try to have her committed to a mental institute. Or maybe Aunt Bertha had a lot of money, and family members thought they could have access to their inheritance prior to her natural demise. Whatever the situation, there was a time when mythical Aunt Bertha might be put into a mental institution, even though she did not belong in one.

A hundred years ago, many mental institutions were scary places. Doctors sometimes misdiagnosed or even mistreated the mentally ill. Pharmaceutical remedies had not been developed. And the rules of incarceration were different.

So where are we today, in terms of mental illness and society? According to experts, our nation has "a patchwork relic of disjointed state and federal agencies that frequently steps in the way of people who are seeking care—instead of helping them." That's how a presidential commission described our current mental health care system, according to an article in the September 8, 2008, edition of *The New York Times*.

Dr. Marcia Goin, past president of the American Psychiatric Association, said that the Times' report gave an honest portrayal of a national mental health system in a shambles. She said that many mentally ill people wind up living on the streets. Some lack needed medication that might help them live a normal life. Others go to jail for crimes—some of them petty.

The report also said that 30,000 Americans commit suicide each year—many of these deaths occur because of undiagnosed or untreated mental illnesses. Hundreds of thousands of people attempt suicide each year, and end up hospitalized.

"'It's a horrendous system across the country," Dr. Goin said.

Today, unless a person is considered to be a physical threat to themselves, a physical threat to someone else, or unable to care for themselves, they are free to do whatever they want—as long as they do not break the law.

I had a difficult time understanding and accepting the fact that a person in need of medical help and support often could not obtain it. Julie needed help that she could not provide for herself. Help that she did not even know she needed. Help that she actively resisted receiving.

The way her brain interpreted information, I was a villain. I was trying to put her away, so that I could run off with my mythical new lover. And John, her son, was trying to get her hospitalized for some ulterior motive of his.

Her very illness prevented Julie from understanding that she was ill. And people who did understand her illness and her need for help—family, doctors, even the police—were unable to help her because there were laws that, in effect, prohibit intervention.

Because of past social injustices, along with the curtailment of mental health care budgets, our society has evolved a system that actively prevents many mentally ill people from getting aid. In summary, in order to be treated, the mentally ill must meet one of the following criteria:

- Personally desire treatment—and voluntarily enter a facility,
- Be a physical threat to themselves or others,
- Be incapable of taking care of themselves,
- Be arrested for a crime,
- Be declared legally incompetent by a court (a lengthy, expensive, and challenging option).

Where does this leave a family member who wants the best for their loved one? It leaves you reduced to hoping that nothing bad happens, even if you witness the person in precarious or dangerous circumstances.

I have been trained to anticipate harm—for myself and those I love—and to take appropriate steps to avoid it. But now Julie could not be helped unless she either got worse, or got into trouble with the police.

I remember praying that my wife would have enough to eat, have a warm bed to sleep in, not be mugged or raped. Ironically, I also wished that she would do something sufficiently illegal to get medical help—before she was hurt or killed.

Exercise 9: Legal Issues v. Mental Health Care

Do you have a situation that falls into this legal No Man's Land? If you do not have anything in this area that is upsetting to you, then skip this Exercise

It is designed to bring internal complaints and struggles to the surface so that you can begin to heal. You need to free yourself from the influence that such situations and feelings create. The way to do that is to view these situations and feelings clearly.

When you write about an issue, it gives you an opportunity to think and feel deeply about it. Many times people have a reservoir of energy tied up in emotions that they are not consciously aware of. They may think that bringing up this "mud" from the bottom of their emotional lake is creating their discomfort. They may think that if they can just keep problems hidden, out of their awareness, that all will be well.

This is not true. We need to see clearly what is causing our discontent, and once we do, we can begin to transform these complex emotional patterns into something useful.

Does reading this chapter trigger any reaction within you regarding this topic? Do you have your own set of frustrations about similar issues? If so, go to your Notebook and clarify what happened—and why it was a complication for you.

After you complete this Exercise, if you are feeling any strong emotion, please redo the Energy Release Process located in Chapter Three.

Record in your Notebook any thoughts or insights you have about this subject.

10
Making Difficult Decisions from Within

About a month after John and I made our unsuccessful trip to Santa Barbara to help Julie, I received a call from a psychiatrist at the Santa Barbara Mental Health Care Facility. Someone from the hotel where Julie was living had called the police about her. One of her credit cards had reached its limit, and when Julie was told this, she overreacted. Hotel personnel knew that something was wrong, and police and paramedics confirmed it.

Because of that incident, Julie was admitted to the hospital and received professional care. The psychiatrist who called me wanted background information about Julie, so that medical personnel could determine the best treatment. I gladly provided it. I was relieved to know that my wife was still alive, safe, and getting help.

Julie called me about three weeks later—a day or two after she was released from the hospital. She said she did not want to continue living. She could not envision herself living a life that she did not enjoy, a life she felt would not improve, a life she no longer wanted. She said she was going to swim into the ocean where we used to walk Merlin. When she could swim no further she would be unable to return. Drowning, she thought, would provide the peace she so desperately wanted.

"Steve," she said, "you are the one person in the world who loves me enough to let me go. I don't want to live anymore. I'm tired and I can't see my life ever getting any better."

She went on to say that she understood enough about her illness to know that she might never recover. She thanked me for my love, kindness, generosity and companionship. "I never really knew love until I met you," she said. "Now I can go, knowing that I have experienced real love."

I was the only person she could tell this to, she explained, because I was the only person who loved her enough that I would not call the police or try to stop her. She was right; I did love her that much.

I remember thinking that Julie was reasoning more clearly than she had been in many months. She was on medication from her recent hospital visit. She was not delusional, manic, or psychotic. In most ways she sounded like her old self.

Tears streamed down my face as I re-connected emotionally with the woman I loved. It was the first rational conversation we had had in a very long time—and, oddly, it centered around her pending suicide.

If she had seemed irrational, I might have felt different, but in that moment, I knew that if she chose not to continue with her life, it was her decision to make.

It took all of my courage to say goodbye to her in that moment. But, that is what I did. I thanked her for all of the kindness, inspiration and love she had shared with me. I told her that I never knew another person like her—as magnificent as her— and that I felt fortunate to have been married to her for 10 wonderful years.

We said goodbye. I hung up the phone, then sat down on the floor, bewildered. Was this what my life had come to? To say my final goodbye over the telephone to my beautiful, beloved wife, then wait for the police to call to tell me her body had washed up out of the ocean? I experienced a complex set of emotions that night, but I never doubted the decision to give Julie freedom to decide to live or not live.

A few days later I was on our fondly remembered beach with Julie. She had decided to not take that final, fatal swim. Instead, she called to ask if I would drive down from Reno and bring some clothes and personal belongings to her.

We spent two or three days together as friends, getting to know one another again. It was quite peculiar. She was so different, and yet still so familiar.

We had both been through a lot in the previous six months. My goal, initially, was to take her things to her, then return home. Part of me did not want to experience the mania and delusions I feared would follow. I had witnessed the cycle many times, and did not see how anything would be different.

The financial responsibility alone was overwhelming; I was liable for all that Julie spent, yet I had absolutely no control over it.

But after a couple of days of being with her, I wondered what would happen to her. Who would take care of her? Where would she live? How would she be able to maintain her medication and have any chance to recover without my support? My heart had melted. Here was my best friend—the person I loved the most in life—in need of love and support. How could I do anything other than help her? In a spontaneous moment, without really thinking about any consequences I asked: "Julie, do you want to come back with me to Reno?"

Do you have difficult decisions to make? How do we decide what is best for an ill family member? What is best for other family members? What is best for ourselves? I have spoken with individuals who have had to make decisions based upon the safety of their children—emotional safety as well as physical safety. I have spoken with individuals who had to give their approval for electroshock treatment of a loved one. I have heard many reports of those unable to make a difficult decision—until the situation became so intense that they could see clearly what needed to be done, and they found the courage to do it.

I cannot provide rules about how to make the decisions you may be required to make; there are too many variables. Your situation—and that of your family—is unique. But I can tell you that there are some obvious things you can do. Solicit input from family members, friends, and health care professionals. Perhaps enlist the aid of an attorney, or police.

No matter what others counsel, however, ultimately *you* have to make the decisions. Even so-called experts do not always agree as to what should be done. In addition, expert opinions sometimes don't feel right.

Also, when you try to reconcile all the ideas of family and friends, it may be impossible to come to a consensus.

The major decisions I made about Julie were spontaneous, rather than carefully deliberate. When the insight came, it felt correct. It might have been contrary to what my logical mind had been thinking, but it felt right and I acted upon it.

Each of us has a strong intuitive sense, beyond our normal, rational, thinking mind. I am certain that each of you has had this experience at some time in your life. We say things like, "I felt in my gut that it was right," or, "I just knew it somehow." These types of responses are what I am talking about.

When you feel this kind of clarity and insight—about any difficult decision—act upon that feeling. It is your intuition talking, and it likely is the best choice. Here are a few examples of clarity and insight that I acted upon:

- The decision not to try to stop Julie from swimming into the ocean that night felt intuitively right.

  The fact is, I could not have stopped her even if my logical mind had said she needed to be stopped. It was night, she was in Santa Barbara, and I was in Reno. If I had called the police, it would have taken them time to arrive; she most likely would have already drowned. Or she might have told them that she was not thinking of suicide at all; she might have convinced them that *I was the one* with the mental instability! (She had effectively used this strategy a time or two.) But my decision was spontaneous, and in that moment it felt right. Others might argue about my decision, but it felt correct to me.

- Another example of an intuitive decision was when I decided—in September, 2005—to divorce Julie. (This was prior to her phone call from Santa Barbara in October.)

  The credit card bills had climbed to about $100,000, and they were growing. And I was liable. Julie and I were not in contact very often. When she did call, she usually was irrational and asking for money. The biggest factor in my evaluation to divorce was that despite all of my efforts to help Julie, our lives were in the same state of disruption as the first night on the bathroom floor when her condition first become apparent to me. The only changes were the increased debt, confusion, and uncertainty.

  I clearly remember the insight that gave me permission to file for divorce: "What would I want Julie to do if our situations were reversed?" My answer was immediate and unwavering: I would want her to get a divorce and get on with her life. I would deal with my life as best I could, but I would not want to hold her in my personal hell.

Does that mean that I would advocate that others with a similar situation file for a divorce? No. Instead, I suggest you get in touch with *your* core values, your inner resources, your inner knowing.

Use the Exercises you are learning in this Guidebook to become still and calm. Allow your decisions to come from that place. Your decisions will be personal. Your family situation is different. Your ill family member is different.

I provide personal examples only as an illustration of how insights came to me—and how I chose to act upon those insights.

- Here is another example of following my intuition. The day before I was to sign divorce papers, I received the phone call from the Santa Barbara psychiatrist—following her hotel-related breakdown. After talking to the psychiatrist, I called my attorney and told him to put the divorce on hold. The psychiatrist's phone call seemed like an omen. I followed my instinct and went to Santa Barbara and met with Julie. It was the right decision for me.

After spending a few days with Julie, I invited her to come back to Reno with me. My logical mind might have argued that nothing would be different, but in that moment, when my heart opened and I extended the invitation to her, my decision felt correct.

We spent about four additional months together in Reno. It was an extremely difficult period. There was even an unsuccessful suicide attempt.

110

Eventually we did divorce. In retrospect, the extra time with Julie convinced me that my decision to divorce was the correct one. The additional four months allowed me to feel certain that I had done everything I could to remain her husband and partner. Because of this I didn't need to spend time second-guessing myself later.

In similar circumstances, you might not feel the same. In fact, you might not agree with any of the decisions I made. That's because everyone has their own unique situations, their own appropriate timing for decisions, their own processes regarding how they will arrive at decisions.

The last idea I want share with you in this chapter is something we addressed in Chapter 3. It deals with guilt and blame. Please do not berate yourself for a decision you already made—or one you failed to make.

It's always easy to go back and look at a past event—knowing what we know now—and say, "I should have done this" or, "I should not have done that." But this is not helpful. Accept the idea that you did the best you could at the time with the information you had.

If you need further support on this, go back and reread Chapter Three and then redo the Energy Release Exercise.

Exercise 10: How to Make Difficult Decisions

For this Exercise, please start with a few minutes of the Breathing Exercise from Chapter Seven or the Energy Release Process from Chapter Three. These are both helpful to get your energy flowing. Use one Exercise or both.

Here is the process I suggest:

1. Consider some simple, non-troublesome decision you need to make. Even if you know how you are going to resolve the issue, you can use it in this Exercise for practice. If you do not have a simple decision to make, invent one such as: "What should I make for dinner tonight?"

2. List possible sources of input that have not already been considered. In the above example you might ask your children, or others who are living with you what they would like for dinner. You might visit the refrigerator and cupboard to see what is already on hand. (When you move into more complicated decisions, you might consult with doctors, therapists, family members, ministers, chaplains, and close friends—people whose opinions and judgment you genuinely respect.)

3. Once you have your input, sit quietly, close your eyes, and use one of the breathing meditations from Chapter Seven to settle yourself. Ask for guidance for the best possible decision about the situation; the decision that will be for the greatest good of all concerned.

Where should you direct this request? If you have a concept of the Divine, direct it there. If you have a special angel or religious figure you resonate with, direct the question there. Some people like to ask their ancestors for input or their soul, or higher self. If none of these feel comfortable, simply ask the universe for guidance. It is not so important where the question is directed, but rather that we are willing to ask it, and then allow for the possibility of new ideas and information to come to us.

Here is the important part: Relax, with no expectation, no anxiety, no agenda. Enjoy your meditation time, finish it, then go about your day or evening.

You may find that insight comes during your meditation time. You may find that it does not.

You may get an answer in a very surprising way—such as reading something in the newspaper, or hearing a song lyric. Perhaps someone phones you with an idea—something you have not considered before.

This is one of the great mysteries of life: questions we pose earnestly and with an openness to receive often get answered in ways we could never have anticipated.

Questions are answered in *their* time, not *our* time, so be patient. This process is just another avenue of potential input; it is not one we can control, direct, or manipulate.

If you receive an insight, evaluate it on the level of common sense. Would it benefit all concerned, in the highest and best way?

How does this solution feel to you? If you do not know what I mean by this, close your eyes again. Become still inside, and center your awareness in your abdomen.

Think of the new idea while keeping your attention in your abdomen. Does it have a soothing feeling, an energizing feeling in your stomach? Or does it create an upsetting, tight feeling? In general your "gut feel" is a good indicator of the usefulness of ideas.

Practice the above process with simple, easy decisions before you move on to bigger, more important ones. This will build your confidence with the process.

This Exercise is designed to provide us with ideas and input that may not have been available to us through conventional means. But you still need to be open to input from conventional sources. Just be receptive to all input.

Record in your Notebook any ideas or insights
you have about this process.

11

Finding Calm in the Eye of the Storm

Weather systems can cause turmoil. Hurricanes, for instance, occur when a particular pattern of related elements combine in a specific way: temperature, wind velocity, humidity, dew point, barometric pressure, jet stream, and the contour of the land.

Scientific understanding of the components of a hurricane is the reason that such storms have become predictable.

One interesting fact about hurricanes is that at their center is the "eye of the storm." In it, the forces of the storm are balanced. There is stillness, quietness, peace.

Highly trained pilots, known as Hurricane Hunters, venture into hurricanes to gather meteorological information. The Washington.com Weather Post said this about the process:

"Once the meteorological equipment pinpoints the storm center, the crew determines the easiest way to get inside. In a well-developed storm, this can be a difficult challenge. Winds at flight level often exceed 100 miles per hour, and the wall cloud surrounding the center can be 10 to 15 miles thick. Rain often comes in torrents, and updrafts and down drafts are usually strong and frequent. Inside the eye, however, the conditions are much different; many times the ocean is visible and there is blue sky and sunshine above. The flight-level winds are nearly calm.

Often the eye and wall cloud presents a stadium effect, like standing in the center of a large football stadium."

Can you get a sense of this description? Like standing in the center of a large football stadium, the winds are whirling all around the stadium, but they do not affect you. You are standing where it is calm; you are standing in the sun; you are standing where it is safe.

I am going to lead you through the next Exercise which will help you find the eye of *your* hurricane - that quiet center on the stadium floor.

Exercise 11-A: The Stadium Exercise

Start with the Meditation from Chapter Seven. Use whichever style of meditation you feel settles you the most. Do this for a few minutes, then continue with this calming Exercise.

Go to your Notebook and begin adding ideas around the perimeter of a new page, starting at the top left. Write any thought that comes to you, regarding your current situation. Draw a circle around the idea you just wrote down. Now write down your next thought and draw a circle around it, and then your third thought, and so on.

Do not judge the idea as positive or negative. Do not censor any thought; every thought has a reason for being there. If an idea pops into your mind, write it down. This is your personal confidential journal; you can record any idea you choose.

Here is what it will look like in pictorial form. I've added some sample comments, to give you the flavor of this Exercise. You can have as many comments and circles as you can fit around the page.

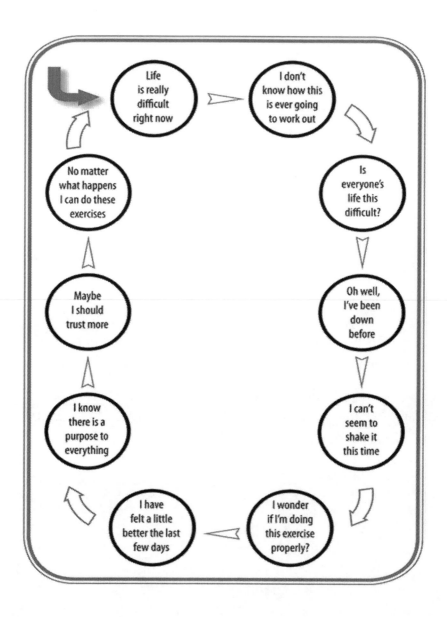

Exercise 11-B: Adding a Summary Thought

The second step is to place a "Summary Thought" in the center of the stadium. Do this after you finish your idea circles. Glance around the circles and survey what you wrote. Here is what typically happens—and what will happen for you if you do this Exercise repeatedly: Regardless of the negative emotion you might be feeling when you begin jotting down your thoughts, when you have gone completely around the stadium you will see that your thoughts have become more positive, more hopeful, more empowering.

I don't know why this works, but it does.

By the time you finish, you will have a more positive "Summary Thought" to place in the middle.

The one which popped into my mind is: "I always get through every experience somehow."

Place your own Summary Thought in the center of the stadium, like the example on the next page.

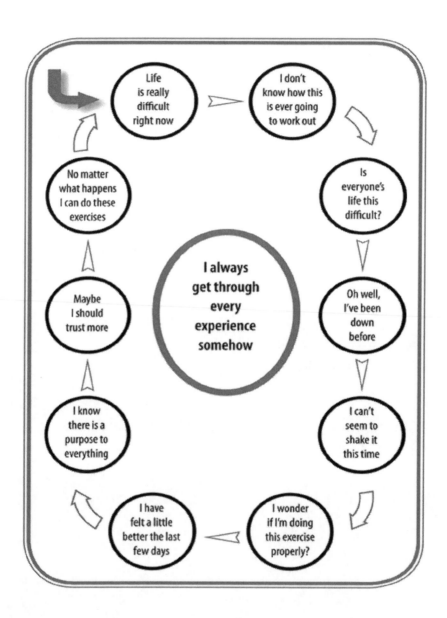

Exercise 11-C: Connecting it All Together

The final part of the Stadium Exercise is to go around the
stadium and draw a connecting line between each "Idea Circle"
and the "Summary Thought" at the center of the stadium.

Here is the best way to do it: Read the statement in the first idea
circle aloud, then draw a connecting line to the Summary
Thought, and read it aloud. In the above example, with the ideas
I placed in my circles, I would say, "Life is really difficult right
now"—(draw the connecting line)—"but I always get through
every experience somehow." The second one I would repeat
would be: "I don't know how this is ever going to work out"—
(draw the connecting line)—"but I always get through every
experience somehow."

Look at the next page to see what it will look like when you are
finished.

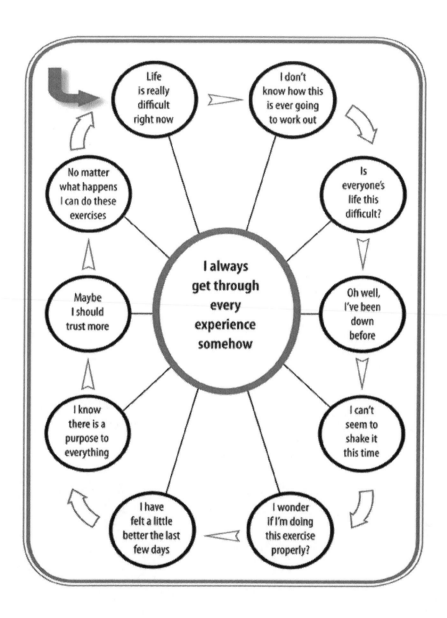

———————

Exercise 11 D: Conclusion

When you have gone completely around the circle and connected your perimeter idea circles with your Summary Thought, close your eyes and find your center, down on the quiet playing field. Imagine that you are in the center of the stadium, in the quiet eye of the storm. Remember, disquieting ideas may be whirling around the stadium, the winds may be howling, but you can find this quiet place within yourself.

I know that it is there, because I have found it within myself. I know it is there for you, because it is within everyone. Even if you have not yet experienced it clearly, it is still there. It is always there.

We can never get away from it, but it can become obscured— particularly during challenging circumstances. You can use the Breathing Exercise from Chapter Seven to help you connect with this quiet place. Feel yourself in the eye of the storm as you focus on your breath. The winds are blowing fiercely, but you are calm and serene in the center. You are safe. You are comfortable. You are a *witness* to the turmoil around you— much like the flyers who witnesses a hurricane from the quiet eye of the storm.

Go ahead and experience this fully.

**Please use your Notebook to record any ideas
or insights that you may have had.**

———————

Part III

Setting the Stage for the Rest of Your Life

12
Living from Your Center

My life changed forever on April 26, 2005. That was the day when my wife, Julie—the woman I loved and was married to for 10 years—left and never fully returned. She developed a severe mental illness and is still in treatment. She has coherence and balance periods from time to time, but the personality I knew and loved has never completely recovered.

This is but one example of how life's difficulties can be overwhelming. In situations such as this we may feel devastated—because the past is gone, and we do not know what the future holds. An emotional hurricane has destroyed all that we know, and the rebuilding has not yet been completed. Perhaps it is not even started.

These are never comfortable times, because of the uncertainty. As humans, we like to feel that we are in control of our lives. Most of us do not like surprises, at least not of this type. We want to know where we will sleep tonight; where we will work tomorrow; where we will take our next meal.

Only after our basic needs have been met do we have time and energy to pursue other interests. When basic needs are not met, all our attention goes toward fulfilling them.

If a hurricane (physical or emotional) comes and wipes out all we know, we are left in No Man's Land. We feel out of control, uncertain about our future. We are at a tactical disadvantage. The howling winds that destroyed the reality that we knew are winds of change.

In the wake of devastation, we are left with not only the cleanup, but also the opportunity—and the need—to rebuild. Probably something can be saved, but many items may not be salvageable. Much depends upon the strength of the storm.

What do we wish to create in the aftermath? We have choices. We no longer have the life we once had, so how will we go about rebuilding?

Do you remember the story of the beggar sitting on the box of gold from Chapter 7? Our own form of gold—a quiet place of peace, contentment, joy and power—is within us constantly. But at this moment, it may seem impossible to find. But when you discover it, it will be a good foundation on which to start any type of reconstruction.

Unfortunately, many have yet to find their inner calm. It does not occur to us to look for ways to quiet down when we are overwhelmed. Nonetheless, this inner source of wisdom can provide answers to even the most difficult questions or problems.

This innate capability has nothing to do with religion, or beliefs, or dogma. It is a reality that lives beyond what we think or believe—and for this reason it is accessible to everyone, at all times.

Take a deep breath and congratulate yourself for the steps you are taking toward your own happiness and empowerment. You are doing this for yourself, and it is valuable to appreciate yourself for it. No one is going to come up and shake your hand for your accomplishment, but we can acknowledge ourselves for our efforts. What we are doing is substantial work.

Now, let's move on to the next Exercise. I think you are going to enjoy this one.

Exercise 12: Living from Your Center

Please begin this Exercise with a few minutes of the Breathing Meditation from Chapter 7, so that you can think from a quiet, centered place.

If you have experienced an emotional hurricane in your life, you need to decide what is left that is salvageable. What would you like to create or recreate in areas that were destroyed? If you had a blank page—on which you could write anything that you would like to create—what would you say? Forget for a moment all the practical considerations, such as "How could I ever do that," or, "How would I pay for that," or "I don't know how to do that."

Have you ever heard the statement, "Begin with the end in mind?" The idea is that before you start any project, job, or task, you have the outcome firmly in mind. Envision the outcome before you begin to work toward it.

There is an innate power all humans have to be creative. Creativity is not limited to artists or inventors or architects. We all have it, and we use it in our everyday lives. Something as simple as finding a parking space downtown can be an act of creativity—and we do not all approach it the same way.

An old adage states: "Thoughts held in mind produce after their own kind." Put another way, what we strongly and persistently imagine helps attract the necessary resources and energy to assist us in bringing about our thought or desire. The key to this principle is to be clear about what we want, and then think about it often—as if it has already happened.

In fact, don't just think about what it is that you desire—actually feel what it feels like to already have it.

I know, it sounds like nonsense! How can I feel as if I have something before I actually have it? The secret is, imagine it! You did it easily as a child. You placed an old blanket over a couple of chairs and you had a military fort. You took a slingshot into your backyard and you were on an African safari. Do you remember those days? It was not hard to do this as a child; your conscious mind did not resist it. In fact you thought it was fun!

You still have this ability.

This Exercise is about using your imagination to help achieve whatever you want. It is the first step in any creative process, and I invite you to begin it now.

Please use your Notebook as an aid in creating a vision of what you desire your future to look like. Have no concern whatsoever as to how you are going to accomplish your goal. The purpose of this Exercise is to create a picture of your future that will get you excited.

It is important to experience in advance what it will feel like when it occurs. Then let go of any attachment you have about how or when it will happen. Your part is to dream it, then step aside to let it happen in its own time and in its own way.

A particularly good time to use this Exercise is just before falling asleep at night. As you are lying in bed, awaiting sleep, allow the thoughts and feelings of "what it would be like if..." to have some time. Use your imagination. Do not concern yourself with the hows, whens and wheres. Make it fun. Do it often.

Vincent Van Gogh said: "I dream my painting, and then I paint my dream."

Let your mind dream your future now.

***Please use your Notebook to record any ideas
or insights that you have.***

13
Embracing Forgiveness: A New Perspective

In order to heal myself, to become whole, I had to learn to forgive. I had to let go of my anger and resentment toward the doctors and lawyers who were in any way involved in Julie's case. If fact, I had to come to terms with the entire mental health care system; a system that sometimes denies medical help to people in desperate need.

Forgiveness is a challenge for everyone. It is difficult to accept behaviors that we consider to be wrong, particularly when those behaviors cause harm. It almost feels as if someone is getting away with their bad behavior—or that we are condoning such behavior—if we forgive them.

Yet we know that resentments we hold toward others create unhappiness within us. And ironically, our resentment often has no effect upon the person we resent. We might think we are punishing another with our lack of forgiveness, but that logic is like drinking poison and expecting the other person to die. Instead, we literally make ourselves ill with such behavior.

I want to introduce a new concept about forgiveness that I have found helpful. As we have discussed throughout this Guidebook, how we think about anything becomes the way we experience it. We also know that we are free to choose any interpretation of each and every event that we experience. This is what we have called "Our Story," in Chapter Six.

Do you remember the concepts? There are facts, and there are interpretations. Facts tend to be limited and indisputable. They actually happened, and generally everyone agrees that they happened. We used the example of two cars colliding. The damage to the cars—bent metal, shattered glass—confirms the reality of the collision.

But then there is the interpretation of these facts. It will differ from person to person, based upon many factors—such as where you were when you heard the crash. Do you have a personal bias, such as the idea that no one should drive over fifty miles per hour? Do you have some other bias that impacts your interpretation?

Our story of any event is derived from our interpretation of the facts, which in turn is based upon our upbringing, culture, family background, past experience, etc. But it is not enough to know this, intellectually. We also must put this knowledge into practice if it is to help us in any meaningful way.

The traditional way of looking at forgiveness is similar to saying: "Bring the guilty bastard to me so that I can forgive him." I have felt this way myself at times. I knew that total forgiveness was the right thing to do, but I could not let go of my need to assign blame. This type of forgiveness is incomplete, and, as such, is not of much value. We are still blaming regardless of the words we say.

You have probably heard the expression, "I can forgive, but I will never forget." This, too, is an incomplete approach. True and complete forgiveness has not taken place. We are still clinging to the concept of wrongdoing and blame.

We have discussed in prior chapters the harmfulness of guilt and blame—especially when we experience them over an extended period of time. We also have explored the idea that each person has his or her own "story" about every event in life. And the concept that everyone's story is "correct"— from his or her point of view.

Given this understanding, can you see the relationship these ideas have to the concept of forgiveness? We have been told since childhood that we need to forgive, but isn't it difficult and sometimes almost impossible to do?

But now I have a wonderful surprise for you. If you do the Exercises in the preceding chapters, *eventually there will be no one left to blame or forgive.* Ultimately, we can learn how to stop blaming ourselves and others. We can learn how to stop holding ourselves and others hostage to some notion we have about how things should have been.

So let's look at this from another perspective. We have been talking about forgiveness from the very beginning in this Guidebook. We have just been using different terminology. The message, however, is consistent: We do not forgive for the sake of the other person. (Who might not even know that know we feel anger or resentment toward them.) We forgive in order to benefit ourselves.

Here is a personal example of this idea:

I had a brother (now deceased) who hurt his wrist in a ninth-grade football game. The injury was not serious at the time, but it caused discomfort later in life. My brother spent 50 years blaming his football coach for the injury and subsequent discomfort. My brother convinced himself that the coach should not have put him into the game for that particular play. Year after year, my brother would speak of the "stupid coach"—and how the coach had done such an irresponsible thing

One day I asked my brother how often he thought about the incident. He said he thought about it maybe once a week.

I then asked him how often he thought that the coach revisited the event. My brother said, "Probably never. The coach is too stupid to know that he did anything wrong."

I then posed this idea to my brother: "Once a week for 50 years is more than 2,500 times that you have felt angry, irritated, aggrieved and resentful. Yet the coach has not felt that way even once. Who's being stupid here?"

To his credit, my brother immediately understood the idea and answered, "I have!"In that moment of honesty, my brother grasped the concept I am presenting here. Better yet he put it into practice. After that day, I never again heard about the football coach. I doubt my brother ever thought about the coach, or the injurious football play, after that. By looking deeper into his own "story," my brother gained a new, more-empowered perspective. A byproduct of this new insight was that there was no one left for him to blame or forgive.

Take a deep breath and digest that last sentence for a moment. Can you sense the power in this concept?

By doing your own internal work, using the Exercises contained in this Guidebook, you can move to a place where there is no one left to blame or forgive.

That is real freedom!

Exercise 13: Forgiveness-A New Perspective

Given the information introduced around the issue of forgiveness in this chapter, it will not be helpful for you to make a list of all those you might resent, and then, in one thundering verbalization declare: "I forgive you all!"

Forgiveness does not work that way, and by now I hope you know this. So here is how I suggest you approach this Exercise:

Begin with something easy. Perhaps someone cut you off in traffic this morning and you still feel irritated about it. Or maybe a neighbor plays his car radio loudly when he drives by your house and you find it annoying. Just pick something minor—not a powder-keg emotional issue—to use as your first Exercise experience.

I want you to get the hang of it, before you take on major forgiveness issues. With minor irritations, you can skip some of the steps below. But for bigger issues, all the steps will be helpful.

Go back and re-read Chapter Six, and then redo the Exercises in that chapter around the specific issue where you feel resentment, anger, etc. Exercise 6-A asks you to write your "story" about the situation—with all the details and emotions, including all the suffering you endured as a result.

Once you complete this, repeat the Energy Release Exercise from Chapter Three. This will clear all the excited energy you may have stirred up.

After writing out the story detailing all your emotions, then, whenever you feel like it, do the second part of the

Exercise, 6-B. This time you will write the same story with no emotion whatsoever.

For a major issue, you may have several pages of detail for 6-A. But perhaps only a few short sentences for 6-B. (When we take all the judgment and emotion out of an issue, often there is not much left to say.)

It is possible that you might require as much as several days to write about a major issue. You might have to write in spurts or stages. If you are unable to complete this Exercise, it just means this particular forgiveness issue is not yet ready to be resolved. Choose something less charged and work on that instead. Come back to the more hurtful situation when you feel ready.

You may need to revisit some events several times, in order to resolve your feelings. It won't necessarily require doing the writing several times, but you might need to redo the Energy Release Exercise multiple times. Highly charged issues, in some cases, may require considerable time to dissipate.

Do not become discouraged. Even if you revisit a situation multiple times, each time you process an incident, you will feel better. Eventually, all of the negative energy associated with that event will be discharged. When that happens, you will be free of it for the rest of your life.

That is real forgiveness. It has the potential to create miracles in your life.

Please use your Notebook to record any ideas or insights you may have had.

138

Chapter 13—Summary Points

True forgiveness sometimes allows us to see that we have, in fact, benefited from our perceived adversary. Consider the football-coach story, for instance. My brother might have chosen to think that the coach provided not an injury, but an opportunity to learn something important; that life involves physical suffering—and many times we cannot do much about that. In my brother's case, the physical suffering was the injured wrist.

But my brother also had a story which created the emotional suffering—which he could control. My brother spent 50 years feeling anger and resentment. He did not create the physical suffering, but he did create the emotional suffering. It was a consequence of his story—his chosen interpretation—of the event.

The coach was the teacher in the sense that he facilitated my brother's learning of an important life lesson. Without the coach, my brother might never have understood the distinction between the suffering of physical pain (which we might not be able to control), and the suffering of emotional pain (which we are often able to control).

I am not suggesting that you should prefer difficult situations. Nor am I saying that you should be happy to receive a severe setback in life. But everyone experiences challenges in life. The important idea here is: how we choose to view our challenges determines how we experience them.

When we are finally ready to let go of the resentment we may have toward someone or something, it is then possible to find that the exact circumstance we have been so angry about, has in fact served us in some meaningful way.

We are going to examine that idea more in the next chapter.

14
Counting the Blessings in this Disaster

Have you ever experienced something that turned out to be a blessing, even though it did not seem that way when it occurred? It is a common theme in many people's lives. We do not always understand the full impact of an event when it is happening; only time can give us the complete perspective. And such insight often requires an open mind to be able to ever discern the benefit.

A few years ago I heard an amazing woman named Candace Cable speak. Candace is a paraplegic who has competed in ten Paralympics Games. In Winter Games she earned nine gold medals, two bronzes and one silver. In Summer Games she added two bronze medals to her collection. She also won 75 marathons as a wheelchair racer—including the Boston Marathon. Six times!

As she addressed her audience, she spoke of the car accident that occurred when she was 21 years old. Candace was paralyzed from the waist down. Try to imagine how devastating this must have felt: twenty-one, and she would spend the rest of her life in a wheelchair.

But this amazing woman did not complain of her loss. Instead, she related highlights of her life—her athletic accomplishments, and the fact she met U.S. Presidents on four separate occasions. She concluded by saying she would never have had these opportunities if she had kept her normally functioning body.

Candace's extraordinary life came about as a direct result of her accident, and subsequent confinement to a wheelchair. She was not even a serious athlete prior to her injury. From her perspective, disaster caused her life to take a dramatic turn for the better. She felt gratitude for the accident, because it provided her the opportunity to become exceptional.

I would like you to take a moment to consider this perspective. Do not personalize it or move into your own situation. Just comprehend what it implies.

Virtually any situation we face can impact us in a variety of ways. Some ways are empowering—they foster growth and satisfaction. Some ways do not. Does everyone who has a serious accident feel the way Candace does? Of course not. Many people in her circumstance would feel angry, depressed, victimized—even decades later. And we can sympathize with that response—especially initially.

But reflect upon some of the concepts we have discussed in this Guidebook: if our overall assessment of our situation does not advance from this perspective of blame, anger, and disappointment, we will continue to experience life from this interpretation. The emotions that we least want to feel, oddly enough, will haunt us forever.

We might be tempted to think we can resolve our negative emotions—that they will go away—if we simply ignore them. But they do not go anywhere, because there is no place for them to go. They will dwell in our minds—they have no expiration date—until we choose to deliberately release them.

If we really want to rid ourselves of unpleasant feelings, we need to take appropriate actions. We must move beyond thoughts that keep us stuck in our unpleasant past. This is the only way change can take place. And we are the only ones who can do it.

Such change must take place in our mind, before it can show up in our physical life. If you don't change your mind, you will never change your life.

One of my teachers said that life is like a tiger: We can never tame it, but we can jump onto its back and ride it—or we can run from it and live in fear forever.

Exercise 14: Counting Your Blessings

If you are a bit upset with this concept of trying to find a blessing buried in disaster, I can totally relate. For years, I did not want to hear any such idea. But I suggest that you use one or more of the Exercises in this Guidebook every time you feel strong negative emotions—regardless of the source. Each time you do so, the negative energy will dissipate. And ultimately, you will no longer react so strongly.

At some point—though not necessarily today—I would like you to complete this Exercise. You will know when you are ready. Whenever you choose to do it, by that time you will be well on your way to recovering your joy and balance. And this Exercise will add to your momentum.

Complete this Exercise when you feel that you have genuine insights as to how even disasters can be transmuted into blessings—when you can honestly say that you have grown in ways that might not have been possible without the negative situation. Do the Exercise when you believe that you have become a different person: stronger, more centered, more capable.

Do this Exercise only when you feel ready.

Look back on all that has happened—including any impact on your career, your finances, etc.—to your loved one, your immediate family, yourself. What have you learned? What have you strengthened? How have you grown as a person?

What positives have you taken from some negative situation, that you now consider to be of value as you continue on your life journey?

__When you feel ready to complete this Exercise, record any insights you have in your Notebook.__

15
Drawing on the Power of Gratitude

It was difficult for me to feel grateful about anything for a long time. I felt too victimized to consider the possibility that my life was really not all that bad. I was in denial, and I wanted to find a magic incantation that would allow me to return to the life that Julie and I had shared.

I even remember thinking one day that if I died, this would be a suitable solution to my problems. I never considered suicide as such, but if I had been diagnosed with a deadly illness—and had only days or weeks to live—I would have felt relief.

Fortunately, death did not come calling. I'm glad that it didn't, because eventually, I worked my way past the anger, confusion, and grief, into gratitude.

Just on the other side of thanklessness is gratitude. Isn't that an amazing concept? In the physical world, everything has an opposite. Hot versus cold, up versus down, large versus small, joy versus sadness, gain versus loss. We may not know how to access an opposite value—at some stage of our lives—but that does not mean that it does not exist.

Gratitude can help us, at any time, to improve all aspects of our lives. It was a fundamental concept espoused by many of the world's great teachers, even if they used different terms to describe it. It is still talked about and written about in many different ways—in both scientific and spiritual communities.

Gratitude is based upon a simple idea: like attracts like. Said another way, what we focus upon expands.

If this is true, then consider the possibility of focusing—for at least a few minutes every day—on what is good in your life. I have a 20-year habit of doing this every night while lying in bed, before falling asleep. Even during my period of deep despair, I spent time each night doing this.

My procedure is to reflect briefly on what I liked about my day. There might be a huge fluctuation, day to day, but there was always something to be grateful for. For example, there has always been enough food for me to eat. Given there are almost a billion people in the world who do not have enough to eat, this in itself is a great blessing. There has always been safe water for me to drink. Even a hot shower was available to me—while half of the world's population doesn't even have running water in their homes, and a quarter of the world's population doesn't have clean drinking water.

Just having the basics of life—food, water and shelter—puts us far ahead of much of the world. When I reflect on these facts, I always have something to feel thankful about.

Some people do more than just think about gratitude, they keep a gratitude journal. They write in it every day. This is a very powerful tool. It has the added benefit of allowing one to repeatedly re-read entries. This is a great daily routine, especially in times of stress. You can use it when things are going well in your life, and also when life's road gets bumpy.

There is a simple reason that gratitude is powerful: what we focus upon expands.

But being positive—about much of anything—can be difficult when we feel excessively negative about our life. At such times, it's hard to sit down and think about or write about why we are grateful. If this is the way you presently feel, take a few minutes to do the Energy Release Exercise from Chapter Three, or the Breathing Exercise from Chapter Seven, or the Stadium Exercise from Chapter Eleven. These Exercises are there for you to use any time, and they can be used over and over.

Use one or more of the Exercises regularly. They are not something to accomplish, like a homework assignment in school, and then never done again. They are included in this Guidebook because they are powerful ways to transform the energy patterns that are keeping you unsettled. I have used these Exercises for years—in both good times and bad.

Now you too have these tools, to create more joy and contentment in your life.

If you were certain that feeling grateful really would improve your life, would you practice gratitude? That's like asking: if a genie jumped out of a lamp and told you that you could have something you wanted simply by asking for it, would you try asking?

It's almost that simple. Practice a few minutes of gratitude every day for a month. See what happens. It's possible that you will continue for the rest of your life.

Exercise 15: What I Feel Grateful for Right Now

Begin practicing gratitude right now. I want you to see how powerful this process is. You attract more of what you desire in life, simply by feeling grateful for what you already have.

Use your Notebook to record anything for which you feel grateful. It might pertain to your past—such as being grateful that you had a loving grandparent when you were young. Or you might appreciative living in a country where most people have a level of freedom that much of the world's populace does not enjoy. Or you might feel grateful for something as simple as sunshine—or a good friend, or the song of a bird, or a beautiful flower.

It can be anything.

If nothing comes to mind, look around at your surroundings. All of it can arouse in us a feeling of appreciation. Have fun with this!

*Please use your Notebook to record any ideas
or insights you may have had.*

16
Rewriting Our Story

You are the authority in your own life—regardless of what you might have been taught when you were a child. The word "authority" comes from the same root as "author," and "authentic." This means you decide what things mean to you.

No one can do this for you—though some might try.

You are at a crossroads as to how you perceive your situation, and the choices you make will determine how you experience your situation.

In my situation with Julie, I spent months avoiding, worrying, justifying, blaming (myself and others), trying to find solutions. Ultimately, this was of little value, and nothing significant changed.

Over time, however, I began to integrate new ideas into my thinking. As I did so, the strain and worry decreased. That helped me to realize that the illness that Julie had developed—however unusual and disruptive it might be—was not outside the natural scope of life.

When our lives are not going ideally, it is easy to label a difficult situation as a mistake. And when we judge something to be wrong or unacceptable, we begin to push against it. This resistance, this *pushing against*, is what causes the majority of the discomfort and confusion we experience.

As human beings we all have things that we naturally enjoy—and things that we do not. But this is not restricted to humans. Have you ever seen a cat that liked to be out in the rain? Cats don't like being wet, yet it still rains. Life as we know it could not exist without rain. Trees, flowers and crops need rain. Even cats require fresh water to stay alive; they may not like rain, but they ultimately are served by it.

It's the same with humans. We are served by all of life's experiences, even if we don't realize that fact when we experience something that we dislike.

The real power in any situation is always our interpretation of that situation. Our comfort or discomfort depends to a large extent upon what we say about the situation, about ourselves, and about others who might be involved with it. Sometimes strong negative thoughts appear to have a life of their own, and initially we may not be able to exert much control over them. As we have discussed throughout this Guidebook, however, there are always multiple ways of looking at any situation.

There is our quiet center—where we can go to regroup, refresh, and gain new insight and understanding.

We can use the Energy Release Exercise from Chapter Three when we feel overwhelmed or have strong negative emotions.

We can re-work the Stadium Exercise from Chapter Eleven and the Breathing Exercises from Chapter Seven to help us gain a new perspective—a perspective that frees us for more joy and contentment.

Initially, when we first experience a disturbing event, we may feel that we have no control or options. We may feel completely engulfed by the situation. All of our energy may be needed just to keep from drowning, emotionally.

This is what I initially experienced when Julie became ill. I felt I had no control over my thoughts or emotions. Over time, however—after the initial shock settled—I came to remember that we do have choices. And that the choices we make either empower us or diminish us.

Sometimes—simply out of habit, or lack of knowledge to the contrary—the easiest choice is to feel victimized by our situation. It may be tempting to never move beyond this negative emotional viewpoint.

A more powerful alternative, however, is to begin to take our "story" apart—the one about our situation. We can look at it from different angles. Write about it, first with as much emotion as possible, and then just the bare facts with no emotion at all. (See Exercise 6-A & 6-B.) By doing this, we develop new options, new patterns of thought. In fact the brain itself forms new neural connections—connections that support our more expanded point of view.

I have traveled this road myself, and I know the way home. If you use these Exercises, this book will become your roadmap to greater peace, clarity and empowerment.

It is not wrong to remain angry or sad, but it certainly is not much fun. It cuts us off from all the good things available to us. Being preoccupied with a past, unpleasant event—long after it has occurred—prevents us from moving forward. In one sense, life is always waiting for us, so there is never a hurry to move forward. On the other hand, however, you are looking for healing and a greater sense of freedom. That's why you purchased this Guidebook. You are ready to move through this situation or you would not be reading this at this time. You found this material because you want to understand and utilize the information contained in these pages.

Regardless of your past, and what might be going on in your life right now, you have in this Guide a set of tools that can be of value to you for the rest of your life. The ideas contained here will help not only with your current situation (mental illness in your family), but also with many other life challenges. These tools and Exercises will work equally well with any difficulty you will ever encounter.

Exercise 16: Rewriting Your Story

What is the most significant or useful idea that you found in this Guidebook?

Do you now feel that you have more control over your life than you did? Do you now feel that you have more choices available to you?

Have you been able to find some relief from all of the pressure and worry you may still feel from time to time?

Have you experienced a positive shift after doing some of the Exercises?

What is your bottom line? Reflecting upon all that you have experienced while going through this material, what is the single, most important thing you can do to improve your current situation.

*Please use your Notebook to record any
ideas that you may have.*

17
Creating Your New Life

Has your life turned out the way you expected? If you look at your high school yearbook, and read all those hopeful and encouraging comments from your classmates, have they all happened? Mine certainly did not. I achieved more in many areas than I expected—and less in others.

I never thought I would divorce twice. I thought I would marry my sweetheart and be with her all my life.

I never thought I would lose my job, or have financial difficulties, or have a mental illness in my family.

I never considered any of that. I thought life would just be wonderful. And when I consider it, overall, it has been! It's not been what I expected, but it has been amazing. It's had many outstanding experiences—and some challenges that have helped me to grow.

It's been a journey. And like any journey, there have been many unknowns, many unexpected twists and turns.

I've had the good fortune to travel extensively, in many parts of the world. One thing I've learned, as a consequence, is that you never know what to expect when you leave your front door. In a foreign country, particularly, you may feel less comfortable or safe than you did at home. The language, currency, customs and traditions may be strange to you. I have experienced all this, yet I wouldn't give up a single travel experience I've had.

I think that life in general is a bit like traveling in a foreign land. It is a journey in which we attempt to control as much as we can. We plan for and work toward things we find meaningful. But at the same time, we realize that we cannot control everything.

In the end we find we are all given the opportunity to re-evaluate many of the ideas we thought were permanent—often on-the-fly.

We are seldom able to have what we want in every situation. But if we can flow along with the currents of life, we gain a sense of resiliency. We can bounce back more readily from any hardship. Conversely, if we do not learn to adapt, to accommodate some of life's challenges, then we become angry, embittered and despondent. Supple trees bend with the wind, rigid ones often break. People are like this too.

My goal in creating this Guidebook is to alleviate suffering within the families of the mentally ill. I have shared with you both my personal experiences and my 30 years of education and training. The ideas and practices contained in this Guide have helped me to survive some devastating situations. Because of that, I believe that they can help you too.

If you will use this book as an on-going resource and redo the Exercises from time to time—particularly those you may have found difficult—your life will gradually improve. The more you use the Exercises, the greater the benefit.

But please be easy with yourself and with this material. Healing is a process. It occurs in its own time. There is no need to rush, or push hard, to achieve anything. In fact, this extra effort may sometimes get in the way of transformation. Many small steps, taken consistently, will lead you steadily to your destination. Love, joy, and contentment are limitless, and they are designed to unfold throughout our life.

Thank you for coming along on this journey.

Exercise 17: Creating Your New Life

Have you ever thought of your life as a journey? What have been some of the significant milestones along your life's route?

What have you enjoyed most in your life?

What are you most proud of?

If you could only choose one thing, what is it you would like to do next?

What have you learned from this Guide that you would like others to know and understand?

Please use your Notebook to comment about your life's journey—the journey that you have taken so far, and the places you wish to visit before your journey ends.

Epilogue

I continue to live in Reno, Nevada. I have spent the past several years working on this project in the hope that it can assist others. I also continue to teach meditation, perform as a local musician, and am active in a community spiritual center.

Julie has spent the past seven years in a mental health treatment center in the midwest, but just prior to the publishing of this book (November 2014), has moved into an assisted living facility. Her son, who became her legal guardian several years ago lives nearby, and along with his wife and two children, support her in every way they can.

I speak with Julie several times a year over the phone. I too support her in the best way I know. Typically that means just listening to her, telling her that I care for her, and reminding her of her magnificence. Sometimes I tell her that regardless of any outer circumstance to the contrary, her inner beauty will never change. I usually remind her to find something positive to appreciate every day—a flower, the sunshine, the sound of a bird. Occasionally we laugh about some past event that we both find funny. I am proud of her on every level. What she is living with can't be easy.

It has been a long haul for Julie, and everyone in her family is excited and optimistic with the progress she has made. We are all hopeful that she will continue to improve and regain the life that she lost, and heal and prosper on every level.

I last saw Julie in the spring of 2008 and my heart melted. It makes me happy to know that it always will.

24832714R00092

Made in the USA
Middletown, DE
07 October 2015